IEEE Trial-Use Standard for Application and Management of the Systems Engineering Process

Sponsor

Software Engineering Standards Committee of the IEEE Computer Society

Approved December 13, 1994

IEEE Standards Board

Abstract: The interdisciplinary tasks that are required throughout a system's life cycle to transform customer needs, requirements, and constraints into a system solution are defined. This standard applies to a performing activity within an enterprise that is responsible for developing a product design and establishing the life cycle infrastructure needed to provide for life cycle sustainment. It specifies the requirements for the systems engineering process and its application throughout the product life cycle. The requirements of this standard are applicable to new products as well as incremental enhancements to existing products.
Keywords: enterprise, Systems Engineering Detailed Schedule (SEDS), Systems Engineering Management Plan (SEMP), Systems Engineering Master Schedule (SEMS), systems engineering process

---

The Institute of Electrical and Electronics Engineers, Inc.
345 East 47th Street, New York, NY 10017-2394, USA

ISBN 1-55937-496-9

IEEE Standards documents are developed within the Technical Committees of the IEEE Societies and the Standards Coordinating Committees of the IEEE Standards Board. Members of the committees serve voluntarily and without compensation. They are not necessarily members of the Institute. The standards developed within IEEE represent a consensus of the broad expertise on the subject within the Institute as well as those activities outside of IEEE that have expressed an interest in participating in the development of the standard.

Use of an IEEE Standard is wholly voluntary. The existence of an IEEE Standard does not imply that there are no other ways to produce, test, measure, purchase, market, or provide other goods and services related to the scope of the IEEE Standard. Furthermore, the viewpoint expressed at the time a standard is approved and issued is subject to change brought about through developments in the state of the art and comments received from users of the standard. Every IEEE Standard is subjected to review at least every five years for revision or reaffirmation. When a document is more than five years old and has not been reaffirmed, it is reasonable to conclude that its contents, although still of some value, do not wholly reflect the present state of the art. Users are cautioned to check to determine that they have the latest edition of any IEEE Standard.

Comments for revision of IEEE Standards are welcome from any interested party, regardless of membership affiliation with IEEE. Suggestions for changes in documents should be in the form of a proposed change of text, together with appropriate supporting comments.

Interpretations: Occasionally questions may arise regarding the meaning of portions of standards as they relate to specific applications. When the need for interpretations is brought to the attention of IEEE, the Institute will initiate action to prepare appropriate responses. Since IEEE Standards represent a consensus of all concerned interests, it is important to ensure that any interpretation has also received the concurrence of a balance of interests. For this reason IEEE and the members of its technical committees are not able to provide an instant response to interpretation requests except in those cases where the matter has previously received formal consideration.

Comments on standards and requests for interpretations should be addressed to:

Secretary, IEEE Standards Board
445 Hoes Lane
P.O. Box 1331
Piscataway, NJ 08855-1331
USA

IEEE Standards documents may involve the use of patented technology. Their approval by the Institute of Electrical and Electronics Engineers does not mean that using such technology for the purpose of conforming to such standards is authorized by the patent owner. It is the obligation of the user of such technology to obtain all necessary permissions.

Introduction

(This introduction is not a part of IEEE Std 1220-1994, IEEE Trial-Use Standard for Application and Management of the Systems Engineering Process.)

History of the standard

The project authorization request for this standard was approved by the IEEE Standards Board in August 1989. The working group was organized and conducted its first meeting in January 1990. From the period of May 1990 until July 1993 a significant effort was expended to coordinate with a parallel standardization effort within the Department of Defense in preparation of MIL-STD-499B. The intent of the close coordination between the Military standardization project and the IEEE P1220 project was to ensure that the standards represented a consistent view of Systems Engineering. In July, 1993 the IEEE P1220 Working Group focused on issuing the standard for balloting. The balloting process was initiated in late December 1993, and was closed out in June 1994.

Because this standard is recognized as being the first commercial standard to address the Application and Management of the Systems Engineering Process this standard will be issued as a trial-use standard. It is anticipated that a joint effort will be undertaken over the next two years to merge this standard and the commercial version of MIL-STD-499B currently being prepared by a joint working group of CODSIA (Council of Defense and Space Industry Associations), NCOSE (National Council on Systems Engineering), and government members. It is anticipated that the commercial version of MIL-STD-499B will be published by the EIA (Electronic Industry Association) as an interim standard.

Objective of this standard

This standard defines the requirements for an enterprise's total technical effort related to development of consumer products (including computers and software) and processes that will provide life cycle support. It prescribes an integrated technical approach to engineering a system and requires the application and management of the systems engineering process throughout a typical product life cycle. This standard defines the disciplined systems engineering process that is to be applied and managed during a systems engineering effort. This process is applied recursively to the development or incremental improvement of a consumer product to satisfy market requirements and to simultaneously provide related life cycle processes for product development, manufacturing, test, distribution, support, training, and disposal.

The concept of systems engineering embodied in this document provides an approach for product development in a system context. It is not meant to describe what an organizational entity called *systems engineering* does; or a job position for which a system engineer is responsible. Rather it encompasses what all organizational entities and all enterprise personnel must accomplish to produce a quality, competitive consumer product that will be marketable, will provide an acceptable return on investment to the enterprise, will achieve customer satisfaction, and will meet public expectations.

The fundamental systems engineering objective is to provide high-quality products and services with correct performance features at an affordable price and on time. This involves the establishment of an integrated set of products (hardware, software, data, facilities, and material) and processes (services and techniques) that are acceptable to customers and satisfy enterprise and external constraints, and considers and defines the role of people in developing, producing, testing, handling, operating, and supporting the system's products and processes. This objective is achieved by simultaneous treatment of product and process content to focus project resources and design decisions for the establishment of an effective system design. This involves an integrated handling of all elements of a system, including those related to manufacturing, test, distribution, operations, support, training, and disposal.

It is not within the scope of this standard to address the roles, responsibilities, training requirements, or related aspects associated with an enterprise's implementation of systems engineering. Such topics provide the "how to implement" details, and thus, are best left to the enterprise for implementation. This standard solely addresses "what" the systems engineering process is, and how it must be applied and managed throughout the system life cycle.

At the time this standard was completed, the Working Group on Systems Engineering Management had the following membership:

Richard Schmidt, *Chair* **Ken Ptack,** *Editor*

Jim Armstrong
Dr. George Friedman
Bill Gess
Jim Lacy
Dr. Jerry Lake
Joel O'Rourke
John Snoderly

Other individuals who have contributed to the development of this standard are:

Jim Cloud
Roger D. Larson
Dr. Arnold M. Ruskin
Jack Sivak

Other individuals who contributed review and comments are:

Hu Cheng
Peter Eirich
Gregg Giesler
April Gillam
Ramzi Haraty
Diana Kang
Ed Kulas
H. Reiche
David Schultz
J. J. Selis
Jim Swanek
L. Mark Walker
Peter F. Zoll

In addition, this standard was coordinated with the following organizations:

AIA
ASC X3
ASQC
Department of Defense
EIA
ISO/IEC/JTC1/SC7
MSC
NNCC
SSC10

The following persons were on the balloting committee:

Frank Ackerman
Mark Amaya
Motoei Azuma
Edward E. Bartlett
Oddur Benediktsson
H. R. Berlack
Richard E. Biehl
Mark Bilger
William J. Boll, Jr.
Sandro Bologna
Ronald Braun
Bruce Brocka
Fletcher Buckley
Susan M. Burgess
Juan R. Cacho
Jaya R. Carl
Neva M. Carlson
Leslie Chambers
Basilio Chen
John Chihonek
Tsun S. Chow
François Coallier
Lee Cooper
G. M. Cornefert
Geoff Cozens
Taz Daughtrey
Paul I. Davis
Felix De Onandia
Bostjan K. Derganc
Rodney Dorville
Einar Dragstedt
Scott P. Duncan
Mokhtar El Asaad
Caroline L. Evans
Richard L. Evans
Richard Farley
John W. Fendrich
Peter Fillery
Jay Forster
Kirby Fortenberry
Richard C. Fries
Eitan Froumine
Simon Gabrihelidis
Barry L. Garner
Yair Gershkovitch
Adel Ghannam
Shirley A. Gloss-Soler
John Garth Glynn
Rajeev Goel
Julio Gonzalez Sanz
Donald Gotterbarn
Michael P. Guba
David Gustafson
Jon Hagar
Walter L. Heimerdinger
Manfred Hein
John W. Horch
Garland M. Jett
David Johnson
Frank V. Jorgensen
Laurel V. Kaleda
Fumimiko Kamijo
Eiichi Kaneko
Richard Karcich
John Kellerman
Ron S. Kenett
Judy Kerner
Scotty Kilbourne
F. L. King
Peter Klopfenstein
Dwayne L. Knirk
Shaye Koenig
Joan Kundig
Lak Ming Lam
John B. Lane
Boniface Lau
Dennis J. Lawrence
Bertil Lindberg
Michael Lines
William M. Lively
Ben Livson
James J. Longbucco
Joseph Maayan
Jukka Marijarvi
James W. McClean
Patrick McCray
Russell McDowell
Sue McGrath
Christopher McMacken
Glen A. Meldrum
James A. Miller
Louis E. Miller
Rajko Milovanovic
Celia H. Modell
Hironobu Nagano
Dennis E. Nickle
Michael O'Neill
Mike Ottewill
Robert Parys
David E. Peercy
Alfred H. Perschel
Peter T. Poon
Robert M. Poston
Kenneth R. Ptack
Ali Rahimi
Meir Razy
John Reddan
John P. Riganati
Gregory Russell
William N. Sabor
Kenneth G. Salter
Ronald K. Saltgaver
Douglas Schaus
Peter E. Schilling
Richard F. Schmidt
Norman Schneidewind
Gregory D. Schumacher
Leonard W. Seagren
Carl S. Seddio
Terry Shepard
Keith Shewbridge
Robert W. Shillato
Katsutoshi Shintani
David M. Siefert
Ronald Skoog
Richard S. Sky
Michael W. Smith
Harry M. Sneed
Alfred R. Sorkowitz
Vijaya Srivastava
Richard Staunton
Richard Stevens
Richard H. Thayer
Douglas H. Thiele
Leonard L. Tripp
Margaret Updike
Ted J. Urbanowcz
Glenn D. Venables
Peter Voldner
Ronald L. Wade
Dolores Wallace
John W. Walz
Camille S. White-Partain
Paul R. Work
F. D. Wright
Natalie C. Yopconka
Weider D. Yu
Janusz Zalewski

Contents

IEEE

IEEE Trial-Use Standard for Application and Management of the Systems Engineering Process

1. Overview

1.1 Scope

This trial-use standard defines the interdisciplinary tasks that are required throughout a system's life cycle to transform customer needs, requirements, and constraints into a system solution. The standard is intended for guiding the development of systems (which includes computers and software) for commercial, government, military, and space applications. This standard applies to a performing activity within an enterprise that is responsible for developing a product design and establishing the life cycle infrastructure needed to provide for life cycle sustainment.

This trial-use standard specifies the requirements for the systems engineering process and its application throughout the product life cycle. The requirements of this standard are applicable to new products as well as incremental enhancements to existing products. It applies to one-of-a-kind products, such as a satellite, as well as, to products which are mass produced for the consumer marketplace. The requirements of this standard should be selectively applied for each specific system development project. The role of systems engineering within the enterprise environment is described in annex A.

The content of this standard describes an integrated approach to product development, which represents the total technical effort for

a) Understanding the environments and the related conditions in which the consumer product will be utilized, and for which the product must be designed to accommodate
b) Defining the consumer product requirements in terms of functional and performance requirements, quality factors, producibility, supportability, safety, and environmental impacts
c) Defining the life cycle process products for manufacturing, test, distribution, support, training, and disposal, which are necessary to provide life cycle support for consumer products

Given the project's authorization and objectives, the performing activity should establish an Systems Engineering Management Plan (SEMP), Systems Engineering Master Schedule (SEMS), and a Systems Engineering Detail Schedule (SEDS) that provide the planning and scheduling of technical efforts to accomplish project objectives. The SEMP is the main planning document for all project technical efforts and describes the tailored application of this standard. The SEMS, an event-based schedule, and the SEDS, a calendar-based schedule derived from the SEMS, address the development activities for the consumer product, as well as supporting life cycle processes. Thus, within this standard, when the term *system* is used, it implies a total system concept that involves the consumer products and their supporting life cycle processes.

1.2 Purpose

The purpose of this document is to provide a standard for managing a system from initial concept through development, operations, and disposal. The inclusion of computers and associated software in today's products has made the need more acute to engineer each of those products as a total system.

1.3 Understanding this standard

The description of the systems engineering process and its application throughout the life cycle demands the use of a system paradigm to aid the presentation of this material. The terms used to support this paradigm are defined in clause 3. As enterprises gain familiarity with the paradigm, they may substitute more familiar terms that are applicable to their industry or business practices. The *system* paradigm is the foundation of this standard and is described below to support the different uses of the term system.

A system can be viewed as an element of a larger system. The challenge is to understand the boundary of the system that is the focus of the development effort as well as the relationships and interfaces among this system to other systems. Figure 1 depicts how a system may relate to other systems and higher-level systems. On a smaller scale, and the focus of this standard, are product-oriented systems such as the automobile, airplane, or computers.

A system is typically composed of several related elements and their interfaces. Each element may be composed of hardware, software, data, facilities, materials, services, and techniques. Additionally, an element has associated with it the people required to develop, produce, test, distribute, operate, support, or dispose of the element's products or train other people to accomplish their role in a system context. Figure 2 provides a hierarchy of terms for the elements making up a system. This generic system hierarchy is a key concept within this standard because it ties the physical and system architectures, specification and drawing trees, system breakdown structure, technical reviews, and configuration baselines together.

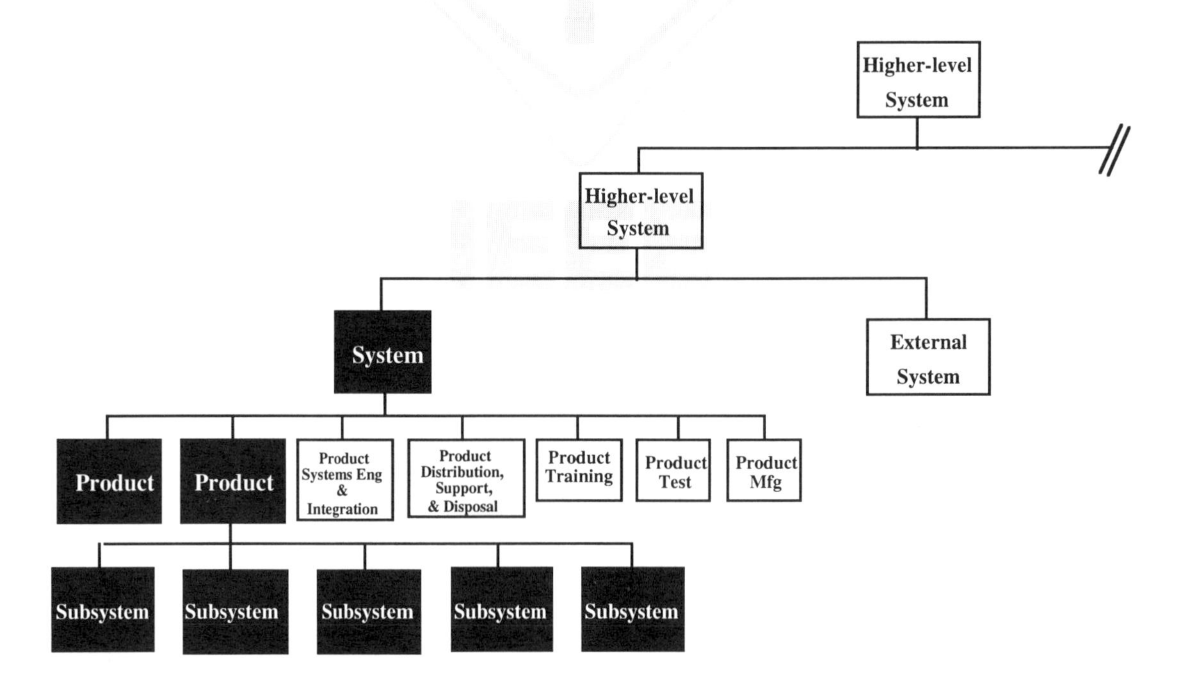

Figure 1—Hierarchy of systems

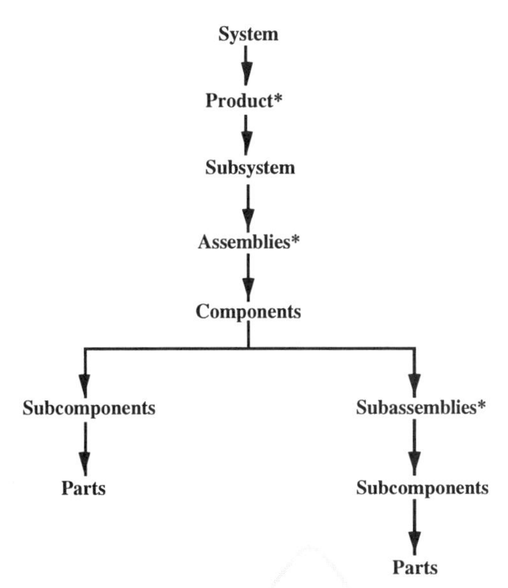

Figure 2—Hierarchy of elements within a system

From a development viewpoint, an actual system may consist of only the first three levels—System, Product, and Subsystems—or it can be composed of multiple levels of elements down to the parts level as shown in figure 2. The basic building blocks of a system—the system, its related product(s), the life cycle processes required to support the products and customers for the product(s), and the subsystems that make up the product(s)—are depicted in figure 3. Each life cycle process—development, manufacturing, test, distribution, support, training, and disposal—is itself like a system in that products must be developed to fulfill the purpose of the life cycle process. For example, a product must be manufactured. Manufacturing is a life cycle process. The products associated with the manufacturing life cycle process include special equipments, tools, facilities, and production processes and procedures.

A typical system is composed of *products* produced by suppliers/subcontractors. Each supplier/subcontractor considers their *product(s)* as part of their *system*. The organization that purchases these *systems* for integration into a higher-level system will refer to these *systems* as subcomponents, components, or subsystems, depending on the significance of the element in contributing to the functionality of the systems or costs.

Figure 4 depicts the three levels of development associated with a total system development. These levels with their associated tasks and outputs are described in clause 5. Note that during system definition the system and its products are defined in specifications, the needs for the life cycle processes are identified, and the subsystems that make up a product are identified and defined in preliminary configuration documents. During subsystem definition each subsystem is treated in the same manner as the system above. The subsystem and its assemblies are fully defined and the need for life cycle processes are identified; and components that make up the assembly are identified and preliminary configuration documents completed. Likewise in component level design, each component may be looked upon as a system with its products (subassemblies) and associated life cycle processes. Each subassembly may have several subcomponents. Component design may continue to be decomposed down to parts or may be stopped at any time at an element of the structure until a point is reached needing no further decomposition to be considered fully designed.

The definitions of system elements are generated by activities of the systems engineering process. This process is shown in figure 5 and described in detail in clause 6. The systems engineering process is used during each level of development to structure systems engineering activities that identify technical requirements and desired system behaviors, and synthesize the system design.

1.4 Organization of this standard

- *Clause 1* provides the scope, purpose, and organization of this standard.
- *Clause 2* lists the standards and acronyms applicable to this document.
- *Clause 3* establishes the meaning of terms as used in this standard.
- *Clause 4* establishes requirements for planning and implementing an effective systems engineering capability within an enterprise.
- *Clause 5* describes of the application of the systems engineering process through system definition, subsystem definition, production, and customer support.
- *Clause 6* details the tasks of the systems engineering process to be tailored and performed to develop consumer product solutions and their supporting life cycle processes.
- *Annex A* discusses the systems engineering process as the total technical effort responsible for establishing the product design and life cycle support products within an enterprise.
- *Annex B* provides a template to help an enterprise prepare a systems engineering management plan.

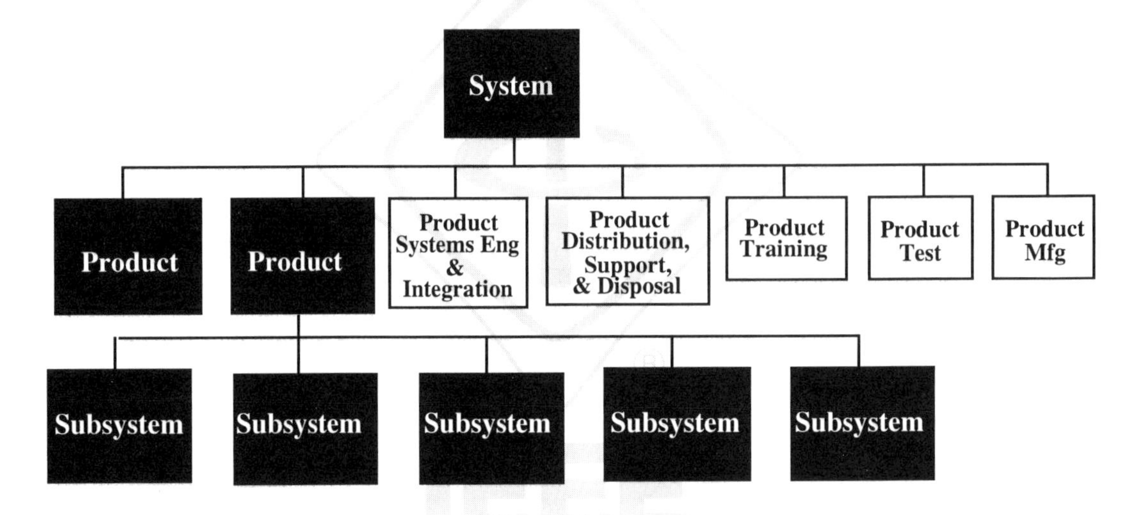

Figure 3—Basic building block of a system

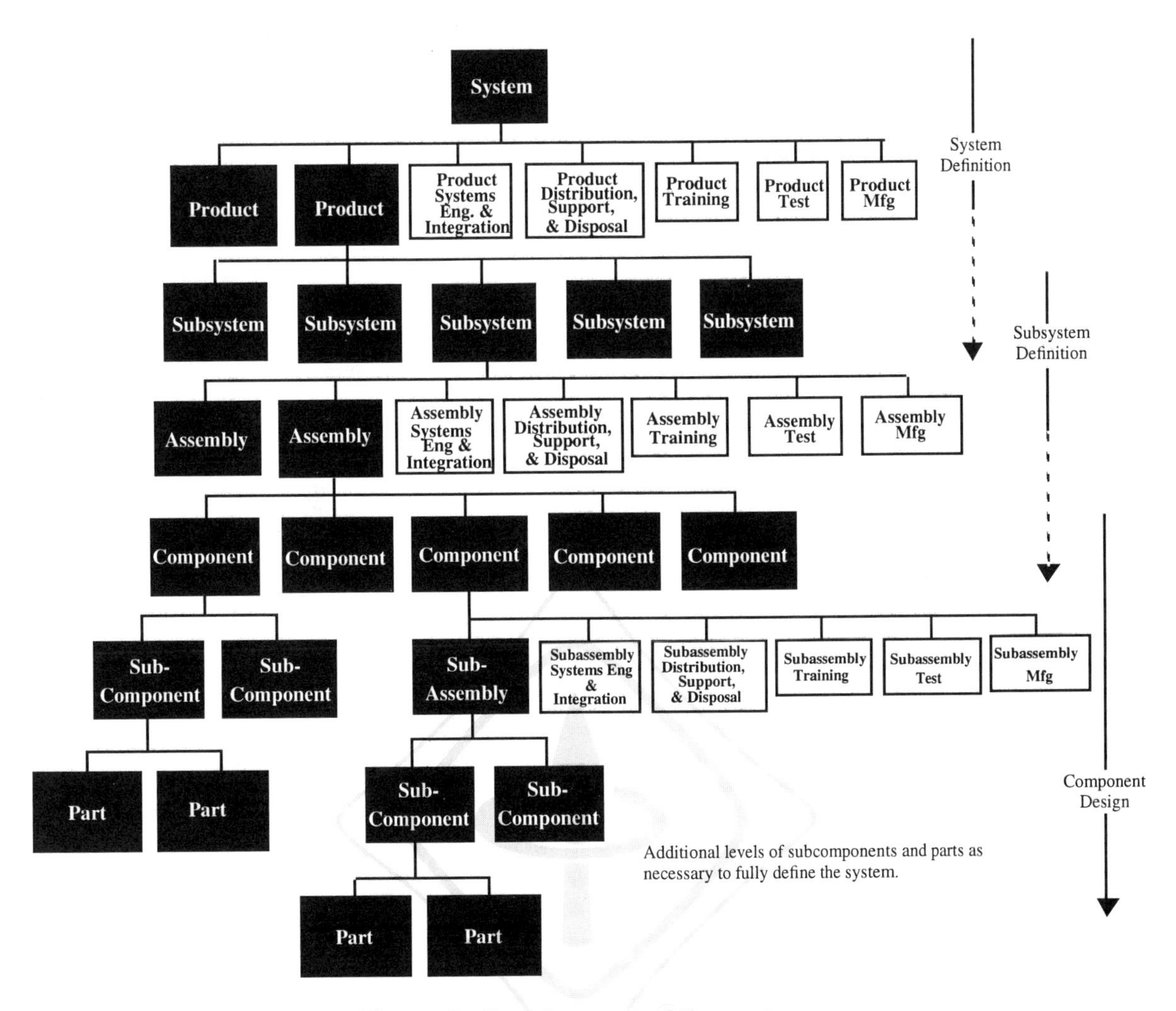

Figure 4—Development of the system

2. References

This standard shall be used in conjunction with the following standards:

ANSI/ASQC Q91-1987, Quality Systems—Model for Quality Assurance in Design/Development, Production, Installation, and Servicing.[1]

IEEE Std 100-1992, IEEE Standard Dictionary of Electrical and Electronics Terms (ANSI).[2]

IEEE Std 610.12-1990, IEEE Standard Glossary of Software Engineering Terminology (ANSI).

IEEE Std 1012-1986, IEEE Standard for Software Verification and Validation Plans (ANSI).

IEEE P1233 November 1993, Guide for Developing System Requirements Specifications.[3]

---

[1]ANSI publications are available from the Sales Department, American National Standards Institute, 11 West 42nd Street, 13th Floor, New York, NY 10036, USA.

[2]IEEE publications are available from the Institute of Electrical and Electronics Engineers, 445 Hoes Lane, P.O. Box 1331, Piscataway, NJ 08855-1331, USA.

[3]This authorized standards project was not approved by the IEEE Standards Board at the time this went to press. It is available from the IEEE.

3. Definitions and acronyms

3.1 Definitions

The definitions listed below establish meaning in the context of this standard. If there is a conflict between IEEE Std 100-1992[4] and this standard, then the definitions provided here should take precedence as they apply only to the practices and requirements of this standard.

3.1.1 assemble: The act of fitting together fabricated or manufactured elements into a larger element.

3.1.2 assembly: An element of the physical or system architecture, specification tree, and system breakdown structure that is a subordinate element to a subsystem and is comprised of two or more components. It represents a consumer product (automatic brake system) of a subsystem (braking system of an automobile); or a life cycle process product (control system) of a subsystem (flight controls of a simulator) related to a life cycle process (training) that supports an assembly or group of assemblies.

3.1.3 behavioral analysis: The analysis of the logical (stimulus/response) and physical (resource consumption, event timing, throughput, etc.) execution of a system to assess the functional and physical architectures.

3.1.4 component: An element of the physical or system architecture, specification tree, and system breakdown structure that is a subordinate element to an assembly and may be composed of two or more subcomponents, or parts; or one or more subassemblies and their associated life cycle processes. In a noncomplex system, the component may be the lowest element.

3.1.5 configuration baseline: The configuration at a point in time recorded in documentation that fully describes the functional, performance, interoperability, interface requirement, and physical characteristics, as appropriate to the stage of the life cycle.

3.1.6 consumer product: An end item delivered to a customer.

3.1.7 constraint: A limitation or implied requirement that constrains the design solution or implementation of the systems engineering process, is not changeable by the performing activity, and is generally nonallocable.

3.1.8 customer: A person or organization ordering, purchasing, receiving, or affected by a product or process provided by the performing activity. Customers include developers, manufacturers, testers, distributors, operators, supporters, trainers, disposers, and the general public.

3.1.9 design (noun): The results of the synthesis process that provide sufficient details, drawings, or other pertinent information for a physical or software element that permits further development, fabrication, assembly, and integration, or production of a product element.

3.1.10 design (verb): The act of preparing drawings or other pertinent information for a physical or software element during synthesis within the systems engineering process.

3.1.11 design-to-cost: Establishes a cost goal that is equivalent to any other performance parameter.

3.1.12 effectiveness analysis: An analysis of how well a design solution will perform or operate given anticipated operational scenarios.

[4]Information on references can be found in clause 2.

3.1.13 effectiveness assessment: The evaluation of the design solution with respect to manufacturing, test, distribution, operations, support, training, environmental impact, cost effectiveness, and life cycle cost.

3.1.14 effectiveness criteria: The measure of value used to determine the success or failure of a design solution.

3.1.15 element: An identified part of a physical architecture, specification tree, or system breakdown structure, including the system itself (see figure 2).

3.1.16 end item: An entity identified with an element of the system breakdown structure. An end item is represented by one or more of the following: equipment (hardware and software), data, facilities, material, services, and/or techniques.

3.1.17 environment: The natural (weather, climate, ocean conditions, terrain, vegetation, dust, etc.) and induced (electromagnetic, interference, heat, vibration, etc.) conditions that constrain the design solutions for consumer products and their life cycle processes.

3.1.18 event-based planning: An approach to establishing project plans, tasks, and milestones based upon satisfying significant accomplishments associated with project events rather than calendar-oriented milestones.

3.1.19 external system interfaces: The system or product interfaces to other systems, platforms, or products that influence the design solutions for consumer products and their life cycle processes.

3.1.20 function: A task, action, or activity expressed as a verb-noun combination (e.g., Brake Function: stop vehicle) to achieve a defined outcome.

3.1.21 functional architecture: An arrangement of functions and their subfunctions and interfaces (internal and external) that defines the execution sequencing, conditions for control or data flow, and the performance requirements to satisfy the requirements baseline.

3.1.22 functional requirement: A statement that identifies what a product or process must accomplish to produce required behavior and/or results.

3.1.23 functional verification: The process of evaluating whether or not the functional architecture satisfies the validated requirements baseline.

3.1.24 integrated database: A repository for storing all information pertinent to the systems engineering process to include all data, schema, models, tools, technical management decisions, process analysis information, requirement changes, process and product metrics, and trade-offs.

3.1.25 integration: The merger or combining of two or more lower-level elements into a functioning and unified higher-level element with the functional and physical interfaces satisfied.

3.1.26 interface specification: The description of essential functional, performance, and physical requirements and constraints at a common boundary between two or more system elements or between a system element and an operator (human interface).

3.1.27 life cycle: The system or product evolution initiated by a user need or by a perceived customer need through the disposal of consumer products and their life cycle process products and by-products.

3.1.28 life cycle cost: The total investment in product development, manufacturing, test, distribution, operation, support, training, and disposal.

3.1.29 life cycle processes: The following eight essential functional processes that may be necessary to provide total consumer satisfaction and meet public acceptance. Once the need for a life cycle process is identified, the life cycle process is treated as a system for the development of life cycle process products and their life cycle processes. The following are the eight essential functional processes.

a) *Development.* The planning and execution of system and subsystem definition tasks required to evolve the system from customer needs to consumer product solutions and their life cycle processes.

b) *Manufacturing.* The tasks, actions, and activities for fabrication and assembly of engineering test models and brassboards, prototypes, and production of consumer product solutions and their life cycle process products.

c) *Test.*

   1) The tasks, actions, and activities for planning for evaluation and conducting evaluation of synthesis products against the functional architecture or requirements baseline; or the functional architecture against the requirements baseline.

   2) The tasks, actions, and activities for evaluating the consumer product solutions and their life cycle processes to measure specification compliance or customer satisfaction.

d) *Distribution.* The tasks, actions, and activities to initially transport, receive, process, assemble, install, test, checkout, train, operate, and, as required, emplace, house, store, or distribute consumer products and life cycle process products.

e) *Operations.* The tasks, actions, and activities that are associated with the use of the consumer product or a life cycle process.

f) *Support.* The tasks, actions, and activities to provide supply, maintenance, and support material and facility management for sustaining operations.

g) *Training.* The tasks, actions, and activities to achieve and maintain the knowledge and skill levels necessary to efficiently and effectively perform operations, support, and disposal.

h) *Disposal.* The tasks, actions, and activities to ensure that disposal or recycling of destroyed or irreparable consumer and life cycle process products and by-products comply with applicable environmental regulations and directives.

3.1.30 life cycle process product: An end item required to perform a life cycle process in support of a consumer product. This end item may be a product, process, or service.

3.1.31 measure of effectiveness (MOE): The metrics by which a customer will measure satisfaction with products produced by the technical effort.

3.1.32 measure of performance (MOP): A performance measure that provides design requirements that are necessary to satisfy an MOE. There are generally several measures of performance for each measure of effectiveness.

3.1.33 method: A formal, well-documented approach for accomplishing a task, activity, or process step governed by decision rules to provide a description of the form or representation of the outputs.

3.1.34 mode: An operating condition of a function, subfunction, or physical element of the system.

3.1.35 operational conditions: The factors, including weather, human operations, external system interactions, etc. that contribute to defining operational scenarios or environments.

3.1.36 operational environment: The natural or induced environmental conditions, anticipated system interfaces, and user interactions within which the system is expected to be operated.

3.1.37 part: The lowest element of a physical or system architecture, specification tree, or system breakdown structure that can not be partitioned (e.g., bolt, nut, bracket, semiconductor, computer software unit).

3.1.38 performance requirement: The measurable criteria that identifies a quality attribute of a function, or how well a functional requirement must be accomplished.

3.1.39 performing activity: The person(s) or organization that performs the tasks specified in this standard.

3.1.40 physical architecture: An arrangement of physical elements that provides the design solution for a consumer product or life cycle process intended to satisfy the requirements of the functional architecture and the requirements baseline.

3.1.41 physical characteristics: The physical design attributes or distinguishing features that pertain to a measurable description of a product or process.

3.1.42 physical element: A product, subsystem, assembly, component, subcomponent, subassembly, or part of the physical architecture defined by its designs, interfaces (internal and external), and requirements (functional, performance, constraints, and physical characteristics).

3.1.43 physical verification: The process of evaluating whether or not the requirements of the physical architecture are traceable to the verified functional architecture and satisfy the validated requirements baseline.

3.1.44 precedented system: A system for which design examples exist within its class, so as to provide guidance for establishing the physical architecture, technical and project plans, specifications, or low risk alternatives.

3.1.45 process: A sequence of tasks, actions, or activities, including the transition criteria for progressing from one to the next, that bring about a result.

3.1.46 product: An element of the physical or system architecture, specification tree, or system breakdown structure that is a subordinate element to the system and is comprised of two or more subsystems. It represents a major consumer product (e.g., automobile, airplane) of a system or a major life cycle process product (e.g., simulator, building, robot) related to a life cycle process that supports a product or group of products.

3.1.47 product and process data package: The evolving output of the systems engineering process that documents hardware designs, software designs with their with their associated documentation, and life cycle processes.

3.1.48 project environment: An environment that defines the objectives, success criteria, project milestones, and associated management priorities that govern the systems engineering activities in support of product development.

3.1.49 re-engineering: The process of improving a system after production through modification to correct a design deficiency or to make an incremental improvement.

3.1.50 requirement: A statement identifying a capability, physical characteristic, or quality factor that bounds a product or process need for which a solution will be pursued.

3.1.51 requirements baseline: The composite set of operational, functional, and physical requirements that serve to guide development and management decision processes.

3.1.52 requirements baseline validation: The process of evaluating the results of the requirements analysis activities of the systems engineering process to ensure compliance with customer expectations, project and enterprise constraints, and external constraints.

3.1.53 risk management: The activities associated with risk management preparation, risk assessment, risk handling option assessment, and risk control.

3.1.54 service: The delivery, installation, maintenance, training, and other labor-intensive activities providing life cycle support associated with the products and processes of the system.

3.1.55 specification: A document that fully describes a physical element or its interfaces in terms of requirements (functional, performance, constraints, and physical characteristics) and the qualification conditions and procedures for each requirement.

3.1.56 specification element: A product, subsystem, assembly, component, subcomponent, subassembly, or part of the specification tree described by a specification.

3.1.57 specification tree: A hierarchy of specification elements and their interface specifications that identifies the elements and the specifications related to physical elements of the system configuration which are to be controlled.

3.1.58 state: A condition that characterizes the behavior of a function/subfunction or element at a point in time.

3.1.59 subassembly: An element of the physical or system architecture, specification tree, and system breakdown structure that is subordinate to a complex component, and is comprised of two or more subcomponents.

3.1.60 subcomponent: An element of the physical or system architecture, specification tree, and system breakdown structure that is subordinate to a noncomplex component, or a subassembly, and is comprised of two or more parts.

3.1.61 subsystem: An element of the physical or system architecture, specification tree, or system breakdown structure that is a subordinate element to a product and is comprised of one or more assemblies and their associated life cycle processes.

3.1.62 system: The top element of the system architecture, specification tree, or system breakdown structure that is comprised of one or more products and associated life cycle processes and their products and services.

3.1.63 system architecture: The composite of the physical architectures for consumer products and their life cycle processes.

3.1.64 system breakdown structure (SBS): A hierarchy of elements and related life cycle processes used to assign development teams, conduct technical reviews, and to partition out the assigned work and associated resource allocations to each of the tasks necessary to accomplish the objectives of the project. It also provides the basis for cost tracking and control. The system breakdown structure is derived from the specification tree.

3.1.65 system effectiveness: A measurement of the ability of a system to satisfy its intended operational uses as a function of how the system performs under anticipated environmental conditions; the reliability and maintainability of system elements; and the ability to produce, test, distribute, operate, support, train, and dispose of the system throughout its life cycle.

3.1.66 system element: A product, subsystem, assembly, component, subcomponent, subassembly, or part of the system breakdown structure that includes the specifications, configuration baseline, budget, schedule, and work tasks.

3.1.67 systems engineering: An interdisciplinary collaborative approach to derive, evolve, and verify a life cycle balanced system solution that satisfies customer expectations and meets public acceptability.

3.1.68 tasking activity: The person(s) or organization that directs a performing activity to accomplish the work specified in this standard.

3.1.69 technical effort: The total engineering, testing, manufacturing, and specialty engineering effort associated with the development of a product that encompasses all of the system, equipment, facilities, etc., necessary for the enterprise to develop, produce, distribute, operate, test, support, train, and dispose of the product.

3.1.70 unprecedented system: A system for which design examples do not exist so that the physical architecture alternatives are unconstrained by previous system descriptions.

3.2 Acronyms

BIT Built-In Test

FAIT Fabrication, Assembly, Integration, and Test

FIT Fault-Isolation Test

FMEA Failure, Modes, and Effects Analysis

IPT Integrated Product Teams

MOE Measure of Effectiveness

MOP Measure of Performance

QFD Quality Function Deployment

SBS System Breakdown Structure

SEDS Systems Engineering Detailed Schedule

SEMP Systems Engineering Management Plan

SEMS Systems Engineering Master Schedule

SPC Statistical Process Control

TPM Technical Performance Measurement

4. General requirements

The enterprise shall plan, implement, and control an integrated technical effort in accordance with this standard to develop a total systems solution that is responsive to market opportunities, specified customer requirements, enterprise objectives, and external constraints. To meet this goal, the enterprise accomplishes the following:

a) Plans, conducts, and manages a fully integrated technical effort necessary to satisfy the general requirements of this standard, as tailored for the specific project
b) Applies the systems engineering process for each level of system decomposition (e.g., concept definition, system definition, subsystem design, fabrication, assembly, integration and test, production, and sustainment)
c) Controls progress through the conduct of
    1) Technical reviews following each level of development
    2) Risk management
    3) Data management
    4) Interface management
    5) Configuration management
    6) Performance-based progress measurement
d) Generates models and prototypes to support trade-off analyses that support system architecting and design
e) Generates a product and process data package which ensures that the product can be produced, tested, delivered, operated, supported, and properly disposed of
f) Captures outputs from all technical activities in an integrated database

4.1 Systems engineering process

The performing activity shall apply the systems engineering process presented in figure 5 to produce the specifications, baselines, and other products as described in clause 5. The systems engineering process is a generic problem-solving process that provides the mechanisms for identifying and evolving the product and process definitions of a system. The systems engineering process applies throughout the system life cycle to all activities associated with product development, verification/test, manufacturing, training, operation, support, distribution, and disposal. Figure 5 depicts the elements of the systems engineering process and shows how they iterate to produce a consistent set of requirements, functional arrangements, and physical solutions. The activities of this process are described in detail in clause 6.

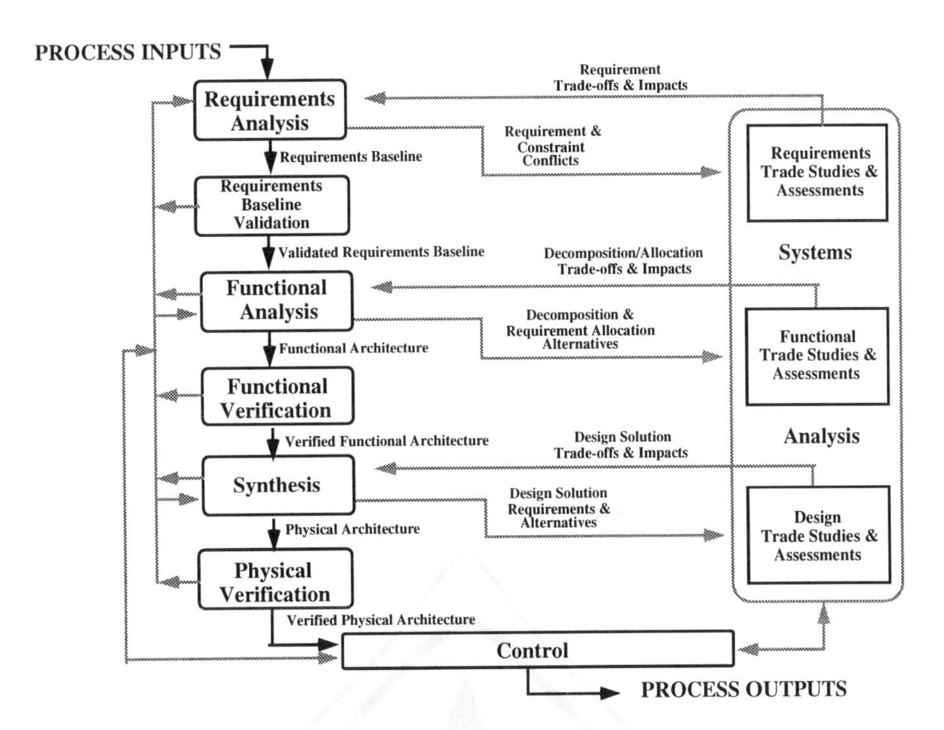

Figure 5—The system engineering process

4.2 Policies and procedures for systems engineering

The enterprise shall develop and maintain policies and procedures for governing the conduct of systems engineering within the enterprise. These policies and procedures specify requirements for the planning, implementation, and control of product development. These policies are selectively applied to varying business segments within the enterprise. Policy existence establishes the enterprise's paradigms for systems engineering, from which training can be based and project specific activities can be communicated. Enterprise policies and procedures shall address:

a) Application of the systems engineering process throughout a project life cycle
b) Preparation and approval of a Systems Engineering Management Plan (SEMP)
c) Preparation and approval of a Systems Engineering Master Schedule (SEMS) and Systems Engineering Detailed Schedule (SEDS)
d) Preparation and approval of an evolving product and process data package
e) Monitoring and reporting technical progress of the project
f) Preparation for and conduct of technical and management reviews
g) Contents and maintenance of an integrated database
h) Continuous product and process improvement

4.3 Planning the technical effort

The performing activity shall prepare, implement, and maintain a Systems Engineering Management Plan (SEMP), Systems Engineering Master Schedule (SEMS), and Systems Engineering Detailed Schedule (SEDS) in accordance with the following subclauses.

4.3.1 Systems Engineering Management Plan (SEMP)

The SEMP guides and controls the technical efforts of the project. The SEMP reflects an integrated technical effort responsible for product development that balances all factors associated with meeting system life cycle requirements. Annex B provides a generic outline and description of the contents for a SEMP. If an evolutionary or incremental development strategy is to be pursued, the SEMP includes an evolutionary development strategy for initial product development and insertion of incremental technology enhancements.

4.3.2 Systems Engineering Master Schedule (SEMS)

The SEMS provides a basis for event-based planning to establish key events, their significant tasks, and the criteria by which completion of significant tasks are determined. A properly designed SEMS allows for the scheduling of activities associated with tasks, loading of resources, budget preparation, assignment of personnel establishing task start and end dates, and event completion dates. The SEMS is structured to ensure that critical technical inputs and decision data are available for technical and project decision points and other identified events, and required progress and system maturity are demonstrated prior to continuing technical efforts dependent on that progress and maturity.

4.3.3 Systems Engineering Detailed Schedule (SEDS)

The SEDS provides a calendar-based schedule of activities, tasks, and key events of the SEMS. This calendar-based schedule is used to track progress and manage resources. SEDS data can be used to construct a network of events, tasks, and activities to determine the critical path of the engineering efforts and to analyze variances to schedule.

4.3.4 Technical plans

Technical plans are prepared to supplement the SEMP as needed. Technical plans are prepared by the engineering and technical specialty areas to which they apply. They are used to implement activities and tasks and to measure technical progress against the plan. Technical plans are typically prepared for risk management, configuration management, technical reviews, verification, computer resources, manufacturing, maintenance, training, security, and safety.

4.4 Evolutionary development strategies

The performing activity shall explore evolutionary development strategies for evolving the system and its capabilities. The capacity to change should be designed into the system architecture to enable the cost effective re-engineering of the system. This design attribute should be established early in the system life cycle to provide a basis for planning each incremental development effort. Evolutionary development strategies offer approaches for managing the introduction of new technologies, evolving requirements, or product capabilities.

4.5 Modeling and prototyping

The performing activity shall establish the models, simulations, or prototypes as required to analyze the system architecture and design, mitigate identified risks, and thereby ensure that the final product satisfies market needs, requirements, and constraints. This effort supports the assessment of the system's functional and performance characteristics, producibility, supportability, environmental impact, safety, and human factors.

4.6 Integrated database

The enterprise shall capture design data in an integrated database to have a repository for the evolving product and process data package, and to provide a shared data source for the exchange and reuse of information.

4.7 Product and process data package

The performing activity shall generate a product and process data package that documents architecture and design information for product manufacturing and life cycle sustainment. The product and process data package includes the types of engineering data defined in table 1. The specific content of the product and process data package is defined early in the project life cycle, and shall consist of the classes of information identified in the subclauses below, and evolves with each application of the systems engineering process to provide more detail with each level of development.

4.7.1 Hardware

The product and process data package includes the technical design information that supports product manufacturing, assembly, and integration.

4.7.2 Software

The product and process data package includes the technical design information that supports software requirements, design, source code, verification and validation, operation, and maintenance.

4.7.3 Life cycle processes

The product and process data package includes descriptions of the life cycle process products related to development, manufacturing, verification, distribution, operations, support, training, and disposal. Example products include special equipment specifications and baselines, software code listings, technical manuals, technical plans, facility drawings, and special tools.

4.8 Specification tree

The performing activity shall generate a specification tree modeled after the verified physical architecture appropriate to the level of development. The specification tree is composed of specification elements and interface specifications. Interface specifications document the interface requirements among interacting physical elements. System interface specifications define interfaces with external systems, platforms, and products. Subsystem interface specifications define interfaces among subsystems. The various specifications that define the elements of a fully developed system are shown in figure 6. Since a performing activity is generally working on an element within a higher-level system, figure 6 reflects how such an effort could be viewed in a system context. The specification tree is developed top down. The number of levels of a specification tree depends on the stage of the life cycle as described in clause 5. The lowest level of the specification tree is dependent upon the complexity of the physical element and to what level the decision can be made to make, buy, or reuse the product associated with the specification. This could be at the subsystem level or any level down to the part level.

4.9 Drawing tree

The performing activity shall generate a drawing tree to reflect the drawings associated with the elements of the physical architecture. This tree should resemble the specification tree of figure 6.

Table 1—Product and process data package content[a]

	Content	Purpose
Hardware	Arrangement drawings	Documents the relationship of the major subsystems or components of the system.
	Assembly drawings	Documents the relationship of a combination of parts and subassemblies required to form the next higher indenture level of equipment or system.
	Connection drawings	Documents the electrical connections of an installation or of its component devices or parts.
	Construction drawings	Documents the design of buildings or structures.
	Product drawings	Documents configuration and configuration limitations, performance and test requirements, weight and space requirements, access clearances, pipe and cable attachments, support requirements, etc., to the extent necessary that an item may be developed or procured on the commercial market to meet the stated requirements.
	Detail drawings	Documents complete end item requirements for the subcomponent(s) delineated in the drawing.
	Elevation drawings	Documents vertical projections of buildings and structures or profiles of equipment.
	Engineering drawings	Discloses by means of pictorial or textual presentations, or a combination of both, the physical and functional end product requirements or design of an item.
	Installation drawings	Documents general configuration and complete information necessary to install an item relative to its supporting structure or to associated items.
	Logic diagrams	Documents by means of graphic symbols or notations the sequence and functions of logic circuitry and flows of sequences for operations, maintenance, test, and repair.
	Numerical control drawings	Documents complete physical and functional engineering and product requirements of an item to facilitate production by tape control means.
	Piping diagrams	Documents the interconnection of components by piping, tubing, or hose; and when desired, the sequential flow of hydraulic fluids or pneumatic air in the system.
	Wire lists	Documents a book-form drawing consisting of tabular data and instructions required to establish wiring connections within or between items.
	Schematic diagrams	Documents, by means of graphical symbols, the electrical connections and functions of a specific circuit arrangement.
	Wiring and cable harness drawings	Documents the path of a group of wires laced together in a specific configuration, so formed to simplify installation.
	Models, simulations, or design databases	Provides a physical, analytical, or digital representation of any of the items listed above.

Table 1—Product and process data package content[a] (*Continued*)

	Content	Purpose
Software	Software design documentation	Documents the software items architecture, design requirements, implementation logic, and data structures that provide a means of support.
	Software source code listings	Documents the actual source code instructions that represented the "as-built" implementation.
Life cycle processes	Process product physical architecture	Documents the physical architecture for the life cycle process products related to development (systems engineering and integration), manufacturing, verification, distribution, support, training, and disposal. Products include equipment, software, facilities, processes, and services integral to a specific life cycle process.

[a]A product and process data package includes, but is not limited to, the items listed in this table.

4.10 System Breakdown Structure (SBS)

The performing activity shall generate a System Breakdown Structure (SBS) modeled after the specification tree (see figure 6). The SBS is used by a performing activity for development and control of work packages, development of planning packages and their conversion to work packages, sizing of work packages, configuration management, resource use, technical reviews, traceability of requirement changes, interface control, cost reporting, and event-based scheduling. The system breakdown structure is a hierarchy of system elements and life cycle processes. Each system element is described by the specification, configuration baseline, budget, work tasks, and schedules related to the element. The life cycle processes are assigned to the product, assembly, and, if needed, the subassembly level of the SBS. The SBS is developed top down. The various system elements and life cycle processes that make up a representative SBS are shown in figure 7. This figure reflects the three major levels of system development—system definition, preliminary design, and detailed design—through which a system evolves as described in clause 5. It also shows the technical reviews typically associated with levels of development. The lowest level of the SBS is dependent on the lowest levels appropriate for the specification tree.

4.11 Integration of the systems engineering effort

The performing activity shall integrate the various inputs of the engineering and business specialties into the systems engineering effort to meet project objectives.

4.11.1 Concurrent engineering

The enterprise should strive to integrate the concurrent design of products and their related processes through the use of an integrated, concurrent engineering environment. Other names for concurrent engineering are team design, simultaneous engineering, concurrent design, or integrated product and process development. Concurrent engineering integrates product and process requirements, organizes a project for efficiency and effectiveness, balances the project's communications infrastructure, and integrates the system documentation infrastructure. Computer-aided engineering tools are used to support development and manufacturing within the concurrent engineering environment. These tools rely on an integrated data repository that contains the system requirements, design information, drawings, etc., as necessary to support the development and production of products.

4.11.2 Integrated teams

Integrated teams are considered as a primary approach to organizing for efficiency and effectiveness. When utilized, the project should assign teams to specific elements of the SBS. Each team prepares required planning documents (SEMP, SEMS, etc.) for the system element to which assigned; is responsible for developing and satisfying the specifications and baselines associated with the element; and completes work outlined in tasking statements related to the element, including the technical reviews of clause 5.

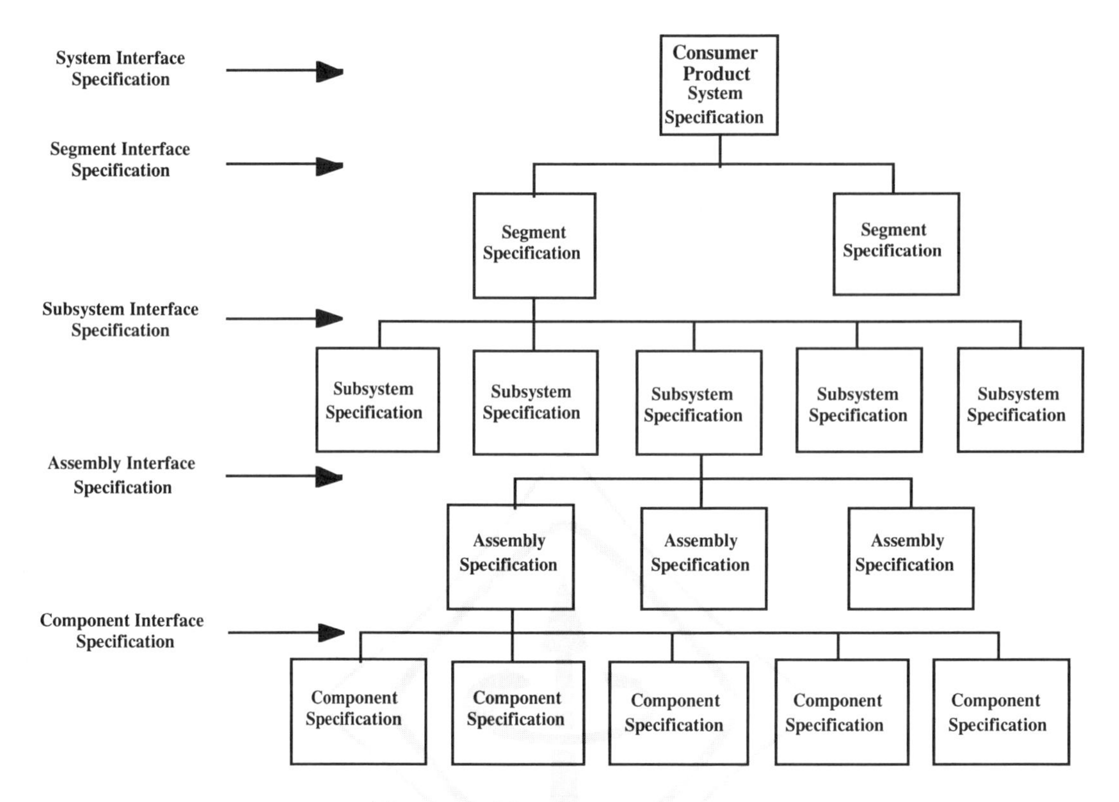

Figure 6—The specification tree

4.12 Technical reviews

The performing activity shall conduct technical reviews, to include design reviews (system, subsystem, component, life cycle processes, test readiness, production approval) and audits (functional and physical configuration), for the purpose of assessing technical progress. Normally, a design review is held at the completion of each application of the systems engineering process.

A review does the following:

a) Assesses the system requirements and allocations to ensure that requirements are unambiguous, consistent, complete, feasible, verifiable, and traceable to top-level system requirements
b) Assesses the design maturity based on technical development goals, systems engineering master schedule events and accomplishments, and empirical analysis and test data supporting progress to date
c) Presents the risks associated with a continued development effort
d) Identifies resources required for continued development
e) Decides whether to proceed with the next application of the systems engineering process, discontinue development, or take corrective action on the products and/or process of the current application before proceeding to the next application.

Component, subsystem, and system design reviews are conducted as appropriate for each level of development. Depending on the complexity of the system, lower-level reviews may be needed (see figure 7). Life cycle process reviews are held for each subassembly, assembly, or product, as appropriate. Trade study and verification results should be available during design reviews in order to substantiate design decisions. Component, subsystem, and system functional configuration audits and physical configuration audits are performed to ensure that tasks, activities, key events, and supporting documentation have been satisfactorily completed; that qualification tests for each specification requirement have been completed and all requirements satisfied; and/or that produced products comply with final drawings.

4.13 Quality management

The systems engineering process shall be documented and applied to develop products and life cycle processes consistent with established quality practices (see ANSI/ASQC Q91-1987).

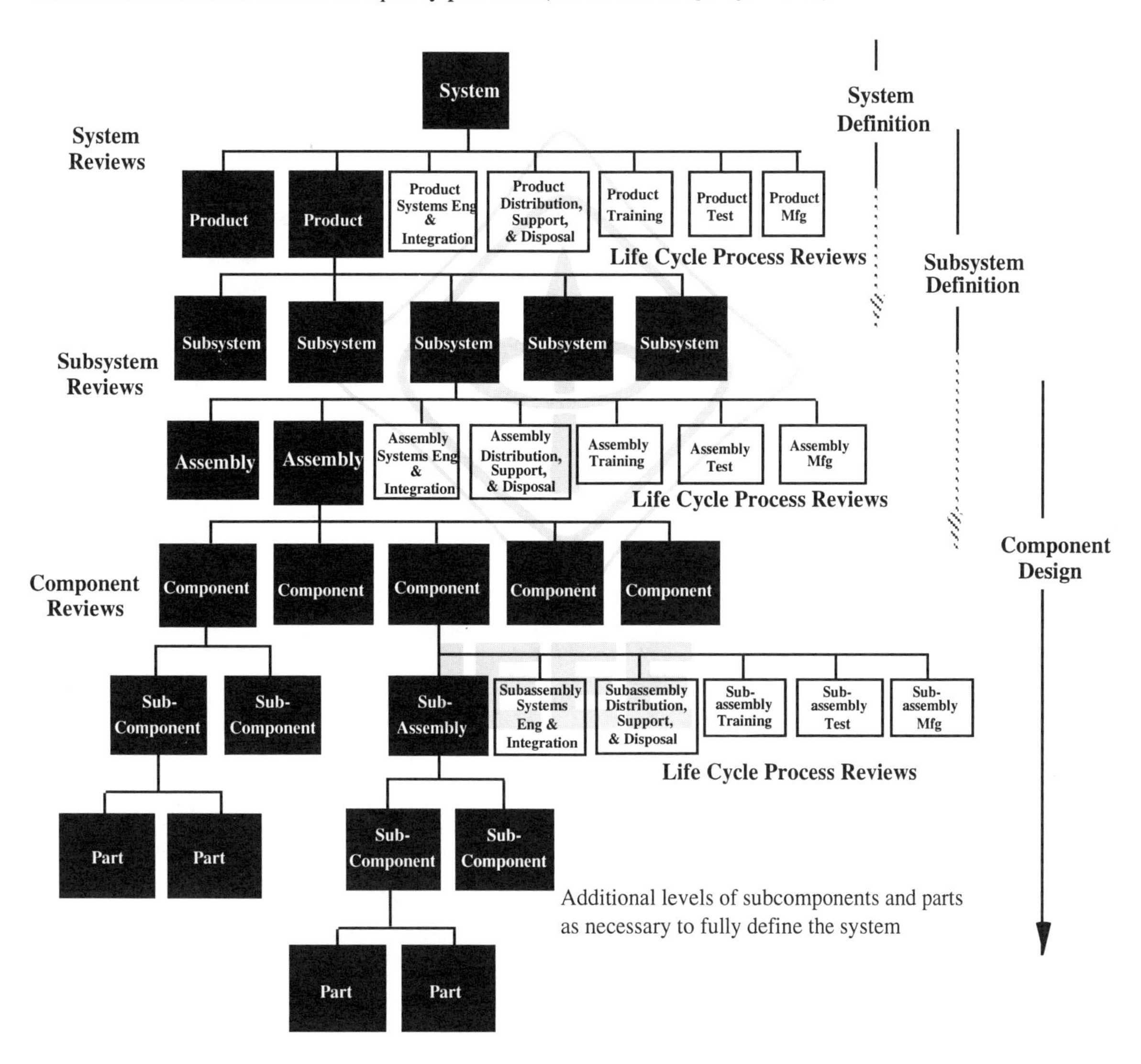

Figure 7—Typical system breakdown structure (SBS)

4.14 Continuing product and process improvement

The enterprise shall maintain a focus that drives a continuing product and process improvement emphasis throughout the system life cycle as described in the following subclauses.

4.14.1 Re-engineering

The enterprise explores ways to improve existing products and processes. Each project should capture the design data, schema, tools, and models related to each development effort and design in the capacity to evolve a product during the customer support stage of the life cycle in order to improve system products and processes and cost effectively correct deficiencies.

4.14.2 Self assessment

The enterprise maintains a rigorous self-assessment program to determine the maturity of its systems engineering practices to include the application of the systems engineering process tasks of clause 6. The enterprise applies insights gained during self-assessment toward improving products, life cycle processes, and enterprise system engineering practices.

4.14.3 Lessons learned

The enterprise captures the lessons learned on each project and incorporates them into enterprise training courses, as appropriate, to improve the application of the systems engineering process. Lessons learned provide a basis for establishing future system development projects, for improving metrics, and for avoiding problems encountered by previous projects undertaken by the enterprise.

5. Application of systems engineering throughout the system life cycle

The performing activity shall apply the systems engineering process (described in clause 6) throughout the system life cycle for development and support of system products and their life cycle processes related to development, manufacturing, verification, distribution, support, training, and disposal. The systems engineering process is applied during each level of system development (system, subsystem, and component) to add value (additional detail) to the products defined in the prior application of the process. The systems engineering process is also applied during fabrication, assembly, integration and test, production, and consumer support stages to resolve reported problems, and for evolving products to improve performance or extend service life. The typical system life cycle stages of development and operations are:

Development

a) System definition

b) Subsystem definition

- Preliminary design of subsystems
- Detailed design of subsystem components
- Fabrication, Assembly, Integration, and Test (FAIT)

Operations

a) Production

b) Customer support

These stages are depicted in figure 8:

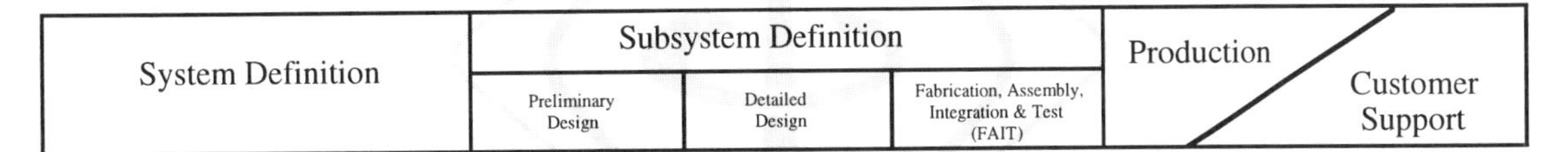

Figure 8—Typical system life cycle

The performing activity satisfies the major exit events for each development stage of the system life cycle as defined in 5.1 through 5.3. These major events include establishing product descriptions, completing specifications, establishing configuration baselines, and completing technical reviews. The performing activity also accomplishes the systems engineering tasks described in 5.4 through 5.5, which includes correcting design and process deficiencies/problems, or evolving the system to provide added capabilities, or to extend the life of the system, and completing technical reviews. Additionally, the performing activity develops the life cycle process products that are needed for system products to satisfy total life cycle needs and requirements. The activities related to life cycle process product developments are discussed in 5.6.

5.1 System definition stage

The purpose of the system definition stage is to establish the definition of the system with a focus on system products required to satisfy operational requirements. The major events of this stage include

a) Completion of system, product and subsystem interface specifications, system and product specifications, and preliminary subsystem specifications

b) Establishment of a system baseline and a preliminary subsystem "design to" baseline

c) Completion of technical reviews appropriate to the system definition stage.

The documents produced during system definition are required to guide subsystem developments. The technical reviews evaluate the maturity of the system development and the readiness to progress to subsystem definition.

5.1.1 System definition

The performing activity shall apply the systems engineering process described in clause 6 for the purpose of generating system-level validated requirements baseline, verified functional and physical architectures, specifications and system baseline, system breakdown structure, and updated project and technical plans. Specific activities to be accomplished are listed in figure 9 and discussed in the following subclauses.

System Definition

SEP*

Establish System Definition
- Select system concept
- Establish initial Project and Technical Plans
- Identify subsystems & subsystem interfaces
- Resolve system risks
- Assess subsystem risks
- Define life cycle quality factors
    - Producibility
    - Verifiability
    - Ease of distribution
    - Operability
    - Supportability
    - Trainability
    - Disposability
- Revise Project and Technical Plans for Preliminary Design

Complete Specifications
- Complete System and Product Interface Specifications
- Complete System and Product Specifications
- Complete Subsystem Interface Specifications
- Complete preliminary Subsystem Specifications

Establish Baselines
- Establish System Baseline
- Establish preliminary Subsystem *Design-to* Baselines

Complete Technical Reviews
- Complete Alternative Concept Review
- Complete System Definition Review

* SEP - Systems Engineering Process Applied to Concept Definition (if necessary) and to System Definition

Figure 9—System definition

5.1.1.1 System concept

For precedented system developments with incrementally improved or evolutionary growth products, the project refines established system definitions to satisfy the market opportunity or customer order. For unprecedented systems where the concept is not already defined, the project creates and evaluates candidate alternative concepts that would satisfy a market opportunity or customer order. One or more of the alternative concepts are selected for further system definition during this first stage of development. The risks associated with each alternative system concept and its products is assessed to include risk identification and quantification. Additionally, preliminary system and product specifications are completed for each alternative along with system and product interface specifications and a preliminary system baseline.

5.1.1.2 Initial project and technical plans

The performing activity establishes necessary project and technical plans for the system life cycle that include a) the activity accomplishment criteria for determining system definition progress assessment and b) the allocation of project resources among the systems engineering activities. The key project plans prepared by the performing activity include the Systems Engineering Management Plan (SEMP), Systems Engineering Master Schedule (SEMS), and the Systems Engineering Detailed Schedule (SEDS). For precedented systems the SEMP, SEMS, and SEDS is prepared for the full development life cycle with the most detail for the current stage. For unprecedented systems the SEMP, SEMS, and SEDS are developed as the system is developed. Related technical plans are developed, as appropriate, for manufacturing, logistics, computer resources, security, safety, reliability and maintainability, and training. Project and technical plans address development of the system products to satisfy the operational functions, as well as development of life cycle process products required to satisfy system-level development, manufacturing, verification, distribution, support, training and disposal functions.

5.1.1.3 Subsystems and subsystem interfaces

The performing activity identifies the subsystems of each product and defines the physical and functional interface requirements among the subsystems and their corresponding performance requirements and design constraints. System product performance requirements are allocated among the subsystems so as to assure requirement traceability from the system products to their respective subsystems and from subsystems to their parent product.

5.1.1.4 System and subsystem risks

The performing activity resolves system-level risks to include products risks that were assessed to be critical to system development during concept selection. For critical risks associated with products, the performing activity utilizes simulation, scale models tests, or prototype tests to demonstrate mitigation of risks to an acceptable level. The performing activity assesses subsystem risks and prioritizes critical risks based upon probability of occurrence and related consequences to cost, schedule, and/or performance.

5.1.1.5 Life cycle quality factors

The performing activity defines the system life cycle quality factors that will influence the system's capability to meet downstream requirements for producibility, verifiability (test), ease of distribution (packaging, handling, transportation, storage, and installation), operability, supportability, trainability and disposability. The system life cycle quality factors are decomposed and allocated among the products and then the subsystems in a manner that ensures that quality factors traceability is maintained.

5.1.1.6 Revised project and technical plans

The performing activity updates necessary project and technical plans in response to changes based on systems engineering process activities conducted during system definition and to reflect planning for the next stage of development.

5.1.2 Specifications

The performing activity shall prepare and control the specifications needed to guide the systems engineering efforts of the system definition stage and the preliminary design stage of subsystem definition (see IEEE P1233 November 1993). The essential specifications are described in the following subclauses.

5.1.2.1 System, product, and subsystem interface specifications

During the initial efforts of the concept/system definition stage, the performing activity completes/refines and places under change control system and product interface specifications. The system interface specification identifies the external functional and physical interfaces for the system with respect to other systems or environmental sensors. External interfaces unique to the selected system concept(s) are defined and documented in the system interface specification in a manner that recognizes the unique nature of these special interface elements. Product interface specifications define the physical and functional interface requirements between products of the system and life cycle processes. The subsystem interface specifications, which define physical and functional interface requirements between subsystems for each product, are prepared and placed under change control prior to completion of system definition. The performing activity identifies which interface requirements provide constraints to system/product/subsystem design and which must have changes managed through interface control working groups.

5.1.2.2 System and product specifications

The performing activity completes and places under control a system specification and for each product of the system a product specification. These system specifications document the system requirements (functional and performance requirements, physical characteristics, and design constraints) and the qualification requirements for each requirement in the system specification. The product specifications document the allocation of system-level requirements to each product, and the qualification requirements for each requirement in a product specification. The qualification sections of each specification identifies the methods that will be used to confirm that each system or product requirement has been satisfied under normal and abnormal conditions.

5.1.2.3 Preliminary subsystem specifications

The performing activity prepares a preliminary subsystem specification for each subsystem identified in the system physical architecture. Preliminary subsystem specifications identify subsystem requirements (the functional and performance requirements, physical characteristics, and design constraints), and the qualification requirements for each requirement in the specification. The qualification section of the specifications should identify the methods that will be used to confirm that each subsystem requirement has been satisfied under normal and abnormal conditions.

5.1.3 Configuration baselines

The performing activity shall prepare and place under configuration control the baselines needed to guide the systems engineering efforts of the system definition stage and the preliminary design stage of subsystem definition. The essential configuration baselines are described in the following paragraphs.

5.1.3.1 System baseline

The performing activity evolves/refines, establishes, and places under control the system baseline. This system-level configuration baseline includes the system interface specification, the product interface specifications, the system specification, the product specifications, and the integrated database, which captures the design, data, models and tools used, metrics, changes, design rationale, and other pertinent information on decisions or clarification made to system requirements.

5.1.3.2 Preliminary design-to baselines

The performing activity generates for each subsystem identified in the physical architecture a preliminary design-to baseline. Each design-to baseline includes applicable subsystem interface specifications, the related preliminary subsystem specification, and any subsystem drawings or sketches developed to define the system's products.

5.1.4 Technical reviews

The performing activity shall plan and conduct applicable technical reviews to assess the maturity of the development effort and to recommend whether the investment should be made to continue the development effort. The system-level reviews completed in this stage of development may be held in conjunction with a project management review.

When Integrated Product Teams (IPTs) are assigned to elements of the System Breakdown Structure (SBS), technical reviews conducted in this stage should be of short duration and attendance should be limited to the integrated team, representatives from interfacing system elements (if needed), and members of the evaluation team. The evaluation team may be the system management IPT or an independent team from another project working on a similar system. Efficiency is to be expected because the development activities being reviewed have had required specialties involved in a cooperative, concurrent effort throughout. In essence, teams are continually reviewing progress to ensure that quality factors are included in specification and baseline documents; that informal verification efforts show progress toward technical requirements and objectives; that required plans are updated as systems engineering process activities are completed; and that risks are incurred or new risks are identified.

5.1.4.1 Alternative concept review

An alternative concept review, if needed, is completed by the performing activity to select a concept or concepts to which the system definition activities described in 5.1.1.2 through 5.1.3.2 are to be applied. During this review each concept is evaluated based on the following:

a) Product and subsystem allocations being reasonable and providing a sound system concept
b) The capability of the concept to satisfy customer requirements and meet public expectations
c) Completion of the system and product interface specifications and preliminary system specification
d) Establishment of a preliminary system baseline
e) The assessed risks associated with the concept
f) The adequacy and completeness of systems analysis data to substantiate decisions made in defining the concept and establishing that the concept will satisfy customer requirements and meet public expectations

5.1.4.2 System definition review

A system definition review is completed by the performing activity at the completion of the system definition stage for the purpose of determining whether the system definition is sufficiently mature to progress to subsystem definition. The system definition is reviewed to ensure that

a) It is sufficiently mature to meet systems engineering master schedule criteria
b) System-level risks have been adequately addressed to justify continued development
c) Trade-study data is adequate to substantiate that system requirements are achievable
d) Decisions made in arriving at the system definition configuration are well supported by analysis, test, and/or other technical data

5.2 Preliminary design stage

The preliminary design stage initiates subsystem design and creates subsystem-level specifications and design-to baselines to guide component development. The performing activity shall apply the systems engineering process for the purpose of decomposing identified subsystem functions into lower-level functions and allocating functional and performance requirements to component-level functional and physical architectures in accordance with the following subclauses.

Each preliminary subsystem specification and preliminary design-to baseline is evolved into a subsystem specification and a design-to baseline, respectively. Preliminary component specifications and preliminary Build-To baselines are defined for the components of the subsystem being developed. Finalized subsystem documents include identification of recommended components and interfaces; resolution of subsystem-level risks; assessment of component risks; and design for quality factors to include, as appropriate, producibility, verifiability, ease of distribution, operability, supportability, trainability, and disposability for each subsystem.

5.2.1 Preliminary subsystem definition

The performing activity applies the systems engineering process described in clause 6 to each subsystem for the purpose of generating subsystem functional and physical definitions. Specific activities to be accomplished are listed in figure 10 and discussed in the following subclauses.

5.2.1.1 Assemblies and assembly interfaces

The performing activity identifies the assemblies of each subsystem and defines the physical and functional interface requirements among the assemblies and their corresponding performance requirements and design constraints. Subsystem performance requirements are allocated among the assemblies so as to assure requirements traceability from subsystems to appropriate assemblies and from assemblies to the parent subsystem.

5.2.1.2 Components and component interfaces

The performing activity identifies the components of each assembly and defines the physical and functional interface requirements among the components and their corresponding performance requirements and design constraints. Assembly performance requirements are allocated among the components so as to assure requirement traceability from the assemblies to their respective components and from components to their parent assembly.

5.2.1.3 Subsystem and component risks

The performing activity resolves subsystem-level risks that were assessed to be critical to subsystem development during system definition, and assesses and resolves assembly risks associates with each subsystem. For critical subsystem/assembly risks, simulations, scale model tests, or prototype tests are used to demonstrate mitigation to an acceptable risk level with respect to cost, schedule and/or performance. The performing activity assesses component risks and prioritizes critical risks based on probability of occurrence and related consequences to cost, schedule, and/or performance.

5.2.1.4 Life cycle quality factors

The performing activity identifies and quantifies subsystem life cycle quality factors that will influence each subsystem's capability to meet downstream requirements for producibility, verifiability (test), ease of distribution (packaging, handling, transportation, storage, and installation), operability, supportability, trainability, and disposability. The subsystem life cycle quality factors are decomposed and allocated among the assemblies and then the components in a manner that ensures that quality factors traceability is maintained.

5.2.1.5 Subsystem drawings

The performing activity completes the preliminary design drawings for each subsystem to satisfy functional architecture requirements as allocated to the subsystem, subsystem interface specifications, and product specifications.

5.2.1.6 Project and technical plans

The performing activity updates necessary project and technical plans in order to respond to changes based on systems engineering process activities conducted during subsystem definition and to reflect planning for the next stage of development.

5.2.2 Subsystem specifications

The performing activity prepares and controls the specifications needed to guide component design activities of the detailed design stage of subsystem definition. The essential specifications are described in the following subclauses.

5.2.2.1 System and product specifications

During the preliminary design stage, the performing activity updates and controls all changes to established specifications. Typically for this stage in the life cycle specifications under control include the system interface specification, subsystem interface specifications, product specifications, and the system specification.

Figure 10—Subsystem definition—Preliminary design

5.2.2.2 Subsystem specifications

The performing activity completes and places under configuration control a subsystem specification for each subsystem. These specifications document the functional and performance requirements for each subsystem, in addition to physical requirements or other imposed design constraints, and the qualification requirements for each performance requirement. The qualification section of individual subsystem specifications should identify the methods that will be used to confirm that each subsystem requirement has been satisfied under normal and abnormal conditions.

5.2.2.3 Component interface specifications

For each product component identified in the physical architecture, the performing activity prepares/refines and places under configuration control component interface specifications. Component interface specifications document the functional and physical interfaces among components that must be satisfied during component development. The performing activity identifies which assembly interface requirements provide constraints to component design and which must have changes managed through interface control working groups.

5.2.2.4 Preliminary component specifications

For each product component identified in the physical architecture, the performing activity prepares/revises a preliminary component specification. The preliminary component specification identifies the functional and performance requirements for the component, in addition to physical requirements, or design constraints, and the qualification requirements for each performance requirement in a preliminary component specification. The qualification section of individual specifications should identify the methods that will be used to confirm that each component requirement has been satisfied under normal and abnormal conditions.

5.2.3 Configuration baselines

The performing activity prepares and places under configuration control the baselines needed to guide the systems engineering efforts of the subsystem definition stage and the detailed design stage of subsystem definition. The essential configuration baselines are described in the following subclauses.

5.2.3.1 System baseline

During the preliminary design stage, the performing activity updates and controls all changes to the system baseline.

5.2.3.2 Design-to baseline

The performing activity evolves/refines and establishes the design-to baseline for each subsystem from the preliminary design-to baseline generated during system definition. This baseline includes the assembly and component interface specifications, subsystem specifications, assembly specifications, and the integrated database that captures the design, data, models and tools used, metrics, changes, design rationale, and other pertinent information on decisions or clarification made to subsystem requirements.

5.2.3.3 Preliminary build-to baseline

The performing activity evolves/refines a preliminary build-to baseline for each component of a subsystem. This baseline includes the component interface drawings and the draft component specification.

5.2.4 Technical reviews

The performing activity plans and conducts applicable technical reviews to assess the maturity of the development effort and to determine whether the investment should be made to continue to the detailed design phase. Technical reviews below the system level should not normally be held as project management reviews, but held as strictly technical reviews.

When Integrated Product Teams (IPTs) are assigned to elements of the System Breakdown Structure (SBS), technical reviews conducted in this stage should be of short duration and attendance should be limited to the integrated team, representatives from interfacing system elements (if needed), and members of the evaluation team. The evaluation team may be the product IPT or an independent team from another project working on a similar subsystem. Efficiency is to be expected because the development activities being reviewed have had required specialties involved in a cooperative, concurrent effort throughout. In essence, teams are continually reviewing progress to assure that quality factors are included in specification and baseline documents; that informal tests verify progress toward technical requirements and objectives; that required plans are updated as systems engineering process activities are completed; and that risks are incurred or new risks are identified.

5.2.4.1 Subsystem reviews

Subsystem reviews are completed by the performing activity for each subsystem at the completion of its preliminary design stage. The purpose of each review is to assure that

a) The subsystem definition is sufficiently mature to meet systems engineering master schedule criteria
b) Component allocations and preliminary component specifications are reasonable and provide a sound subsystem concept
c) Subsystem risks have been assessed and resolved to a level appropriate to continue development
d) Trade-study data is adequate to substantiate that subsystem requirements are achievable
e) Decisions made in arriving at the subsystem configuration definition are well supported by analysis and technical data

5.2.4.2 System review

A system-level review is completed by the performing activity after completion of subsystem reviews. This review is to determine whether the total system approach to detailed design satisfies the system baseline; unacceptable risks are mitigated; issues for all subsystems, products, and life cycle processes are resolved; and accomplishments and plans warrant continued development effort.

5.3 Detailed design stage

The detailed design stage of the system life cycle completes subsystem design down to the lowest component level and creates a component specification and build-to component baseline for each component. The outputs of this stage are used to guide fabrication of pre-production prototypes for development test. The performing activity shall apply the systems engineering process, in accordance with the following subclauses, as many times as needed to decompose identified component functions into lower-level functions and allocate functional and performance requirements throughout the resulting lower-level functional and physical architectures.

Each preliminary component specification and preliminary build-to baseline generated during preliminary design of the subsystem must be evolved into a component specification and a build-to baseline, respectively. Finalized component documents should include identification of recommended parts and interfaces; resolution of component-level risks; and for each component, down to the lowest subcomponent, the design for quality factors to include, as appropriate, producibility, verifiability, ease of distribution, operability, supportability, trainability, and disposability.

5.3.1 Detailed subsystem definition

The performing activity applies the systems engineering process described in clause 6 to each component, and its subcomponents, for the purpose of generating component functional and physical architectures. Specific activities to be accomplished are listed in figure 11 and discussed in the following subclauses.

Subsystem Definition
Detailed Design
SEP...SEP*
<u>Establish Detailed Subsystem Definitions</u> • Complete Component definition • Resolve Component risks • Design in life cycle quality factors • Complete detailed drawings for each component/subcomponent • Revise Project and Technical Plans for Fabrication, Assembly, Integration, and Test <u>Complete Specifications</u> • Update system, product, subsystem, and assembly Specifications • Complete Component Specifications <u>Establish Baselines</u> • Update System and *Design-to* Baselines • Establish *Build-to* Baselines <u>Complete Technical Reviews</u> • Complete Component Detailed Design Reviews • Complete Subsystem Detailed Design Reviews • Complete System Detailed Design Review

* SEP .. SEP - Denotes multiple applications of the systems engineering process to each subsystem component and each component subcomponent

Figure 11—Subsystem definition—Detailed design

5.3.1.1 Component definition

The performing activity decomposes the components of each assembly to a level sufficient for design completeness, completes the definition of each subcomponent and the component, and controls the interfaces among the subcomponents. Component requirements are allocated among the subcomponents in a manner that ensures that requirements traceability is maintained in both directions.

5.3.1.2 Component risks

The performing activity resolves component-level risks that were assessed to be critical to component development during subsystem definition. For critical component risks, simulations, scale model tests, or prototype tests are used to demonstrate mitigation to an acceptable risk level with respect to cost, schedule, and/or performance. The performing activity assesses and resolves subcomponent risks and prioritizes critical risks based on probability of occurrence and related consequences to cost, schedule, and/or performance.

5.3.1.3 Life cycle quality factors

The performing activity identifies and quantifies component life cycle quality factors that will influence each component's capability to meet downstream requirements for producibility, verifiability (test), ease of distribution (packaging, handling, transportation, storage, and installation), operability, supportability, trainability, and disposability. The component life cycle quality factors are decomposed and allocated among the component's subcomponents and then lower subcomponents in a manner that ensures that quality factors traceability is maintained.

5.3.1.4 Detailed drawings

The performing activity completes the detailed design drawings for each component and its subcomponents to satisfy functional architecture requirements as allocated to the component, component interface specifications, and the assembly specification.

5.3.1.5 Project and technical plans

The performing activity updates necessary project and technical plans in order to accommodate changes based on systems engineering process activities conducted during detailed design for subsystem definition and to reflect planning for the fabrication, assembly, integration, and test stage.

5.3.2 Specifications

The performing activity prepares and controls the specifications needed to guide fabrication, assembly, integration, and test activities of subsystem definition. The essential specifications are described in the following subclauses.

5.3.2.1 System, product, subsystem, and assembly specifications

During the detailed design stage, the performing activity updates and controls all changes to approved specifications. Typically for this stage in the life cycle the approved specifications may include the system, subsystem, and component interface specifications; the system specification; and product, subsystem, and assembly specifications.

5.3.2.2 Component specifications

The performing activity completes a component specification for each component identified in the physical architecture. The component specification identifies the functional and performance requirements for the component, in addition to physical requirements, or design constraints, and the qualification requirements for each performance requirement. The qualification section of individual specifications should identify the methods that will be used to confirm that each component requirement has been satisfied under normal and abnormal conditions.

5.3.3 Configuration baselines

The performing activity prepares and places under configuration control the baselines needed to guide the systems engineering efforts of the subsystem definition stage and the detailed design stage of subsystem definition. The essential configuration baselines are described in the following subclauses.

5.3.3.1 System and design-to baselines

The performing activity updates and controls all changes to the established system baseline and to established design-to baselines.

5.3.3.2 Build-to baselines

The performing activity evolves/refines and establishes the build-to baseline for each component from the preliminary build-to baseline generated during preliminary design. This baseline includes the component interface specifications, the component specifications, and the integrated database that captures the design, data, models and tools used, metrics, changes, design rationale, and other pertinent information on decisions or clarification made to component requirements.

5.3.4 Technical reviews

The performing activity plans and conducts applicable technical reviews to assess the maturity of the development effort and to recommend whether the investment should be made to continue into Fabrication, Assembly, Integration, and Test (FAIT). Technical reviews below the system level should normally not be held as project management reviews, but held as strictly technical reviews.

When Integrated Product Teams (IPTs) are assigned to elements of the system breakdown structure, detailed design reviews should be of short duration and attendance should be limited to the integrated team, representatives from interfacing system elements (if needed), and members of the evaluation team. The evaluation team may be the assembly IPT or an independent team from another project working on a similar assembly. Efficiency is to be expected because the development activities being reviewed have had required specialties involved in a cooperative, concurrent effort throughout. In essence, teams are continually reviewing progress to assure quality factors are included in specifications and baseline documents, that informal tests verify progress toward technical requirements and objectives, and that required plans are updated as systems engineering process activities are completed.

5.3.4.1 Component reviews

Component reviews are completed by the performing activity for each component at the completion of the detailed design stage. The purpose of this review is to ensure that

a) Each detailed component definition is sufficiently mature to meet systems engineering master schedule criteria
b) Component specifications are reasonable and provide a sound component concept
c) Component and related life cycle process products risks have been assessed and resolved to a level appropriate to support FAIT
d) Trade-study data is adequate to substantiate that detailed component requirements are achievable
e) Decisions made in arriving at the detailed component definition configuration are well supported by analysis and technical data

5.3.4.2 Subsystem reviews

Subsystem level reviews are completed by the performing activity for each subsystem after completion of component reviews associated with the subsystem. This review is to determine whether the subsystem detailed design satisfies the design-to baseline; risks are mitigated and remaining risks are acceptable; issues for all components, assemblies, and life cycle processes are resolved; and accomplishments and plans warrant continuation with fabrication, assembly, integration, and test.

5.3.4.3 System review

A system level review is completed by the performing activity after completion of subsystem detailed design reviews. This review is to determine whether the detailed design of the system satisfies the system baseline; unacceptable risks are mitigated; issues for all subsystems, products, and life cycle processes are resolved; accomplishments and plans satisfy criteria for continuation of the project; and the system is ready to continue into assembly, integration, and test by having resolved outstanding product, or life cycle process issues.

5.4 Fabrication, Assembly, Integration, and Test (FAIT) stage

The performing activity shall apply the systems engineering process during this stage, in accordance with the following subclauses, for the purpose of resolving product deficiencies when specifications for the system, product, subsystem, assembly, or component are not met, as determined by inspection, analysis, demonstration, or test. The purpose of the FAIT stage of subsystem definition is to verify that the products designed satisfy specifications. The major activities of this stage are shown in figure 12.

5.4.1 System integration and test

Integration is conducted to ensure that the combining of the lower level elements results in a functioning and unified higher level element with logical and physical interfaces satisfied. Test activities are conducted to verify that the system meets system requirements. The performing activity completes this by first verifying the components and then conducting verifications at each level up to and including the total system. The purpose is to progressively assemble and integrate subcomponents into complete components, components into assemblies, assemblies into subsystems, subsystems into products, and then where meaningful, products and their life cycle process products and services into a complete system. At each level of assembly and integration, the components, assemblies, subsystems, products, and system should be subjected to sufficient testing to ensure operational effectiveness, interface compliance, compliance with specified requirements, producibility, supportability, and ease of use. The performing activity is responsible for the proper handling and disposal of test articles and all hazardous wastes generated by tests or used in conjunction with tests.

5.4.2 Analyze, fix, and retest

When an element of the system fails to satisfy its test requirements, the performing activity analyzes the deficiency to determine the cause of the problem and applies the systems engineering process to resolve the problem. The performing activity then retests the product to ensure operational effectiveness, interface compliance, compliance with specified requirements, producibility, supportability, and ease of use.

5.4.3 Project and technical plans

The performing activity updates necessary project and technical plans in order to respond to changes based on systems engineering process activities conducted during the FAIT stage for subsystem definition and to reflect planning for production.

5.4.4 Specifications

The performing activity updates and controls all changes to approved specifications.

5.4.5 Configuration baselines

The performing activity updates and controls all changes to the established baselines.

5.4.6 Technical reviews

The performing activity plans and conducts applicable technical reviews to assess the maturity of the development effort, to determine readiness to conduct qualification testing, and whether the investment should be made to continue into production. Technical reviews below the system level should not normally be held as project management reviews, but held as strictly technical reviews.

When Integrated Product Teams (IPTs) are assigned to elements of the system breakdown structure, technical reviews conducted in this stage should be of short duration. The evaluation team may be the assembly or product IPT or an independent team from another project working on a similar assembly or subsystem.

Efficiency is to be expected because the development activities being reviewed have had required specialties involved in a cooperative, concurrent effort throughout. In essence, teams are continually reviewing progress to assure quality factors are included in specification and baseline documents, that informal tests verify progress toward technical requirements and objectives, and that required plans are updated as systems engineering process activities are completed.

Subsystem Definition

Fabrication, Assembly, Integration & Test

SEP... SEP*

Conduct System Integration & Test
- Buy or fabricate, assemble, integrate, and test components and assemblies
- Assemble, integrate and test subsystems and segments
- Assemble, integrate, and test the system
- Analyze and Fix Failures/Deficiencies and Retest
- Update all specifications and baselines
- Revise Project and Technical Plans for Production

Complete Technical Reviews
- Complete Component Test Readiness Reviews
- Complete Subsystem Test Readiness Reviews
- Complete System Test Readiness Review
- Complete Component Functional Configuration Audits
- Complete Subsystem Functional Configuration Audits
- Complete System Functional Configuration Audit
- Complete Component Production Approval Reviews
- Complete Subsystem Production Approval Reviews
- Complete System Production Approval Review

* SEP ... SEP - Denotes multiple applications of the systems engineering process to correct test failures and/or product/process deficiencies.

Figure 12—Subsystem definition—Fabrication, assembly, integration, and test

5.4.6.1 Test readiness reviews

Test Readiness Reviews (as needed for components, assemblies, subsystems, products, and the system) are completed by the performing activity to assure the following:

a) Test procedures comply with test plans and descriptions, demonstrate adequacy to accomplish test requirements, and satisfy specification qualification requirements
b) Pre-test predictions and informal test results (if any) indicate testing will confirm satisfaction of specification requirements
c) New or modified test support equipment, facilities, and procedural manuals required to accomplish test and evaluation are available and satisfy their requirements
d) Required specification, baseline, and other supporting documentation are complete and accurate

5.4.6.2 Functional configuration audits

Functional configuration audits (as needed for components, subsystems, and system) are completed by the performing activity to verify that respective products have achieved requirements and satisfy the characteristics as specified in specifications, interface specifications, and other baseline documentation, and that test procedures and plans were complied with.

5.4.6.3 Production approval reviews

A system-level production approval review is completed by the performing activity after completion of product functional configuration audits to demonstrate that the total system (people, products, and processes) has been verified to satisfy specification and baseline requirements for each system level, and to confirm readiness for production, distribution, operations, support, training, continuing improvement (if applicable), and disposal. The performing activity confirms that

a) Issues for the components, assemblies, subsystems, products, and life cycle process products and services are resolved
b) Test procedures for components, assemblies, subsystems, and products were completed and accurate
c) The system and products were confirmed ready for test
d) Tests were conducted in accordance with established procedures
e) An audit trail from design reviews held after detailed design is established with changes substantiated and all component, subsystem, and system products meet specification requirements
f) Risk handling procedures are satisfactory for production
g) Evolutionary development requirements and plans have been refined
h) Planning is complete and procedures, resources, and other requisite people, products, and processes are available (or programmed to be available) to initiate production, distribution, operations, support, training, disposal, and evolutionary development (if any)

5.5 Production and customer support stages

The performing activity shall apply the systems engineering process, in accordance with the following subclauses, to correct deficiencies discovered during production, assembly, integration, and acceptance testing of products and/or life cycle process products. The producing activity shall also apply the systems engineering process during customer support to evolve the product to implement an incremental change, resolve product or service deficiencies, or to implement planned evolutionary growth. The major events of these two stages of a product's life cycle are shown in figure 13.

5.5.1 System products

The performing activity performs appropriate production inventory and control activities; production, assembly, integration, and acceptance test activities; and packaging, handling, storage, delivery, and installation activities to provide system products to consumers and support organizations. The performing activity manages suppliers to ensure the timely delivery of quality products, materials, and services needed to carry out production activities.

5.5.1.1 Product and process deficiencies

The performing activity applies the systems engineering process to correct product and/or process deficiencies found during production, acceptance testing, or distribution.

5.5.1.2 By-products and waste disposal

The performing activity ensures the proper handling and disposal of hazardous wastes and materials generated by or used in production, acceptance testing, and distribution. In some cases, enterprises may be responsible for proper disposal of products after completing service life.

5.5.2 Technical reviews

Physical configuration audits (as needed for components, subsystems, and the system) are completed by the performing activity to assure the system elements conform to the technical documentation that defines the build-to baseline.

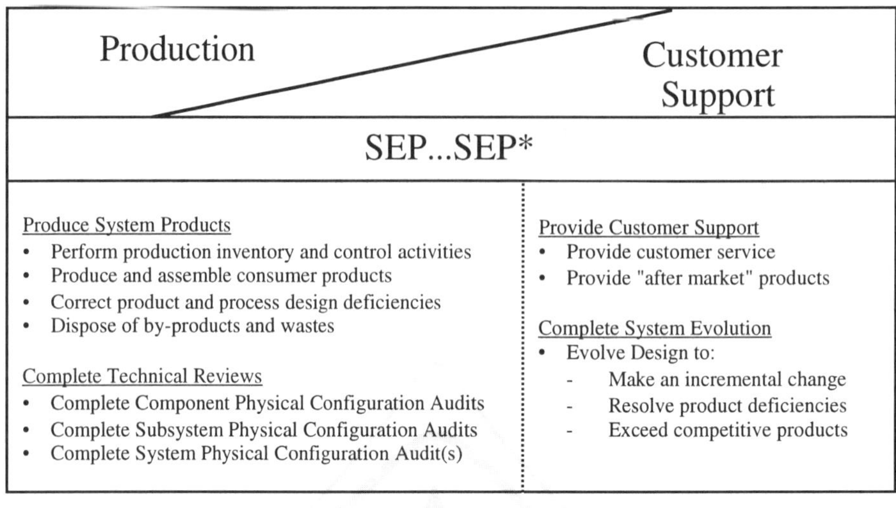

* SEP ... SEP - Denotes multiple applications of the systems engineering process to correct process or product design deficiencies and/or to evolve design

Figure 13—Production and customer support

5.5.3 Customer support

Once products are in the field, the performing activity continues to support customers with needed services and after-market products, and to maintain supplier relationships.

5.5.4 System evolution

The performing activity applies the systems engineering process during customer support to make incremental improvements to fielded products and services; to resolve product or process deficiencies discovered during consumer use of products or during service activities; and to make changes to products and services to compete with products and services offered by competitors.

5.5.4.1 Revise project and technical plans

The performing activity updates necessary project and technical plans in order to respond to changes based on systems engineering process activities conducted during production and customer support.

5.5.4.2 Specifications

The performing activity updates and controls all changes to approved specifications.

5.5.4.3 Configuration baselines

The performing activity updates and controls all changes to established baselines.

5.6 Simultaneous engineering of products and services of life cycle processes

The performing activity shall accomplish planning activities and apply the systems engineering process to develop life cycle process products and services for system product development, production, test, distribution, support, training, and disposal in accordance with the following subclauses.

Life cycle process products and services include such items as

a) Special tooling and equipment for manufacturing or maintenance
b) Special processes for manufacturing; software and hardware for support equipment or training or test simulators
c) Training or maintenance manuals
d) Development, manufacturing, and test plans
e) Facilities for test, manufacturing, or disposal
f) Procedures for services related to each downstream activity

The life cycle process products and services are needed to enable the capability of consumer products to be fully realized throughout their life cycle. Generally, initiation of product and service developments for life cycle processes is delayed until requirements are defined for the products the life cycle processes will support. However, where life cycle process products or service requirements are specified by project or enterprise policies, or by the customer, the definitions of consumer products will be constrained to meet these requirements. The phasing for the simultaneous engineering of life cycle process products and services is presented in figure 14.

Although development of life cycle process product definitions may not be initiated prior to the definition of related consumer products, the performing activity schedules of applicable downstream life cycle process products and services shall be available at the time needed. Since most life cycle process products are not as complex as the consumer product for which they are intended to support, the development cycle should be shorter and the products should be available when needed.

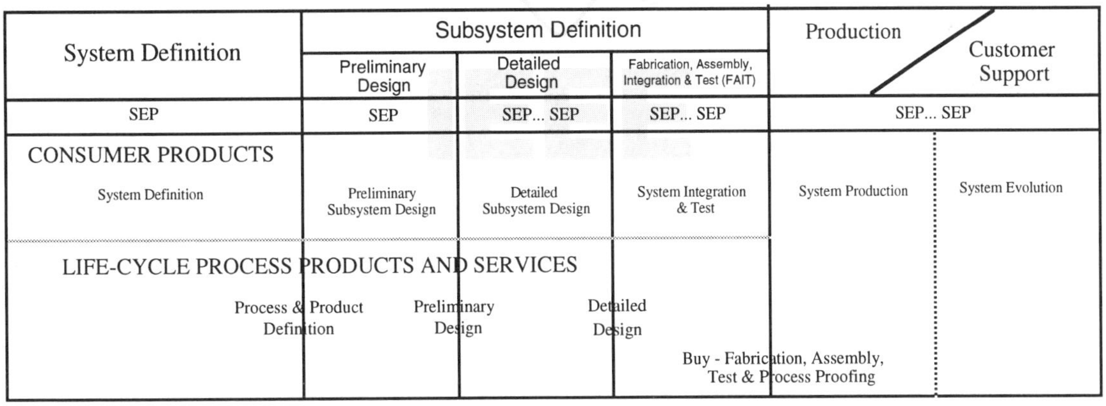

System Definition	Subsystem Definition			Production / Customer Support	
	Preliminary Design	Detailed Design	Fabrication, Assembly, Integration & Test (FAIT)		
SEP	SEP	SEP... SEP	SEP... SEP	SEP... SEP	
CONSUMER PRODUCTS System Definition	Preliminary Subsystem Design	Detailed Subsystem Design	System Integration & Test	System Production	System Evolution
LIFE-CYCLE PROCESS PRODUCTS AND SERVICES					
Process & Product Definition	Preliminary Design	Detailed Design	Buy - Fabrication, Assembly, Test & Process Proofing		

Figure 14—Simultaneous engineering of products for the life cycle processes

5.6.1 Life cycle process product and service development

The performing activity initiates development or procurement of applicable downstream life cycle products and services for development, production, verification, distribution, support, training, and disposal to provide life cycle support to products and their subsystems, and for assemblies and their components. Some more complex systems may require life cycle process products and services for an element below the component level of the SBS in figure 7. Each life cycle process product goes through the same development events and activities as described for consumer products in 5.1 through 5.5, including technical reviews.

5.6.2 Specifications

The performing activity prepares/revises, approves, and controls specifications of the same type as described in 5.1 through 5.5 for the life cycle process products and services related to products, assemblies, or subassemblies as shown in figure 7.

5.6.3 Baselines

The performing activity prepares/revises, establishes, and controls baselines of the same type as described in 5.1 through 5.5 for the life cycle process products and services related to products, assemblies, or subassemblies as shown in figure 7.

6. The systems engineering process

This clause describes the detailed requirements of the systems engineering process (see figure 5). For each subprocess of the systems engineering process, a figure is provided to diagram the general flow of tasks for the subprocess. The performing activity should tailor the activities of each task by adding or deleting activities, or tailor the subprocess tasks by adding or deleting tasks, according to the scope of their project. Specific methodologies, tools, and models need to be generated by the performing activity to accomplish the tailored tasks and activities.

6.1 Requirements analysis

The performing activity shall perform requirements analysis, in accordance with the following subclauses, for the purpose of establishing what the system must be capable of accomplishing; how well system products must perform in quantitative, measurable terms; the environments in which system products must operate; and constraints that will affect design solutions. The market needs, requirements, and constraints are derived from customer expectations, project and enterprise constraints, external constraints, and higher-level system requirements. These are documented in a requirements baseline. The requirements baseline guides the remaining activities of the systems engineering process and represents the definition of the problem that must be solved. The tasks associated with requirements analysis are identified in figure 15. The performing activity assesses and analyzes inputs defined in tasks 6.1.1 through 6.1.9 to identify cost, schedule, and performance risks; to define functional and performance requirements; and identify conflicts. Trade studies are conducted to resolve such conflicts so as to arrive at a balanced requirements baseline. The trade study and risk assessment, analysis, and handling tasks are discussed in 6.7. For each application of the systems engineering process, the performing activity refines previously defined requirements for upper levels of the system architecture, as appropriate, and defines requirements for the system under development (see also 1.3).

6.1.1 Customer expectations

The performing activity defines and quantifies the customer expectations for the system. Customer expectations may come from marketing, a customer order, a recognized market opportunity, direct communications from customers, or the requirements from a higher-level system. Customer expectations include

- What the customer wants the system [product(s) and life cycle processes] to accomplish (functional requirements)
- How well each function must be accomplished (performance requirements)
- The natural and induced environments in which the product(s) of the system must operate or be used
- Constraints (e.g., funding; cost or price objectives; schedule; technology; nondevelopmental and reusable items; physical characteristics; hours of operation per day; on-off sequences; external interfaces; and specified existing equipments, procedures, or facilities related to life cycle processes)

6.1.2 Project and enterprise constraints

The performing activity identifies and defines project and enterprise constraints that will impact design solutions. Project constraints may include

- Approved specifications and baselines developed from prior applications of the systems engineering process
- Updated technical and project plans
- Team assignments and structure
- Automated tools availability or approval for use
- Control mechanisms
- Required metrics for measuring project progress

Enterprise constraints may include

- — Management decisions from a preceding technical review
- — Enterprise general specifications, standards, or guidelines
- — Policies and procedures; domain technologies
- — Established life cycle process capabilities
- — Physical, financial, and human resource allocations to the project

6.1.3 External constraints

The performing activity identifies and defines external constraints that will impact design solutions or the implementation of systems engineering process activities. These constraints include public and international laws and regulations; the technology base; industry, international, and other general specifications, standards, and guidelines; and competitor product capabilities.

6.1.4 Operational scenarios

The performing activity identifies and defines the operational scenarios that define the range of the anticipated uses of system product(s). For each operational scenario, the performing activity defines expected interactions with the environment and other systems, and physical interconnections with interfacing systems, platforms, or products.

6.1.5 Measures of effectiveness (MOE)

The performing activity defines system effectiveness measures that reflect overall customer expectations and satisfaction. Key MOEs may include performance, safety, operability, reliability, and maintainability, or other factors.

6.1.6 System boundaries

The performing activity defines which system elements are under design control of the performing activity and which fall outside their control and the expected interactions among system elements under design control and external and/or higher-level and interacting systems outside the system boundary.

6.1.7 Interfaces

The performing activity defines the functional and physical interfaces to external and/or higher-level and interacting systems, platforms, and/or products in quantitative terms. Mechanical, electrical, thermal, data, procedural, and other interactions are included.

6.1.8 Utilization environments

The performing activity defines the utilization environments for each of the operational scenarios. All environmental factors, natural or induced, that may affect system performance must be identified and defined. Specifically, weather conditions (e.g., rain, snow, sun, wind, ice, dust, fog), temperature ranges, topologies (e.g., ocean, mountains, deserts, plains, vegetation), biological (e.g., animal, insects, birds, fungi), time (e.g., day, night, dusk), induced (e.g., vibration, electromagnetic, chemical), or other environmental factors are defined for possible locations and conditions where the system may be operated.

6.1.9 Life cycle process concepts

The performing activity analyzes the outputs of tasks 6.1.1 through 6.1.8 to define life cycle process requirements necessary to develop, produce, test, distribute, operate, support, train, and dispose of system products under development.

6.1.10 Functional requirements

The performing activity defines what the system must accomplish or must be able to do (the functional requirements). The functions identified through requirements analysis will be further decomposed during functional analysis, see 6.3.

6.1.11 Performance requirements

The performing activity defines the performance requirements for each function of the system. Performance requirements describe how well functional requirements must be performed to satisfy the system measures of effectiveness. These performance requirements are the Measures Of Performance (MOPs) that are allocated to subfunctions during functional analysis and that are the criteria against which physical solutions (derived from synthesis—see 6.5) are measured. There are typically several MOPs for each MOE.

6.1.12 Modes of operation

The performing activity defines the various modes of operation for the system products under development. The conditions (environmental, configuration, operational, etc.) that determine the modes of operation are defined.

6.1.13 Technical performance measures

The performing activity identifies the Technical Performance Measures (TPMs) that are key indicators of system performance. Selection of TPMs should be limited to critical MOPs which, if not met put the project at cost, schedule, or performance risk. Specific TPM activities are integrated into the systems engineering master schedule to periodically determine achievement to date and to measure progress against a planned value profile.

6.1.14 Physical characteristics

The performing activity identifies and defines required physical characteristics (e.g., color, texture, size, weight, buoyancy) for the system products under development. The performing activity identifies which physical characteristics are constraints and which can be changed based on trade studies.

6.1.15 Human factors

The performing activity identifies and defines human factor considerations (e.g., physical space limits, climatic limits, eye movement, reach, ergonomics) which will affect operation of the system products under development. The performing activity identifies which human factors are constraints and which can be changed based on trade studies.

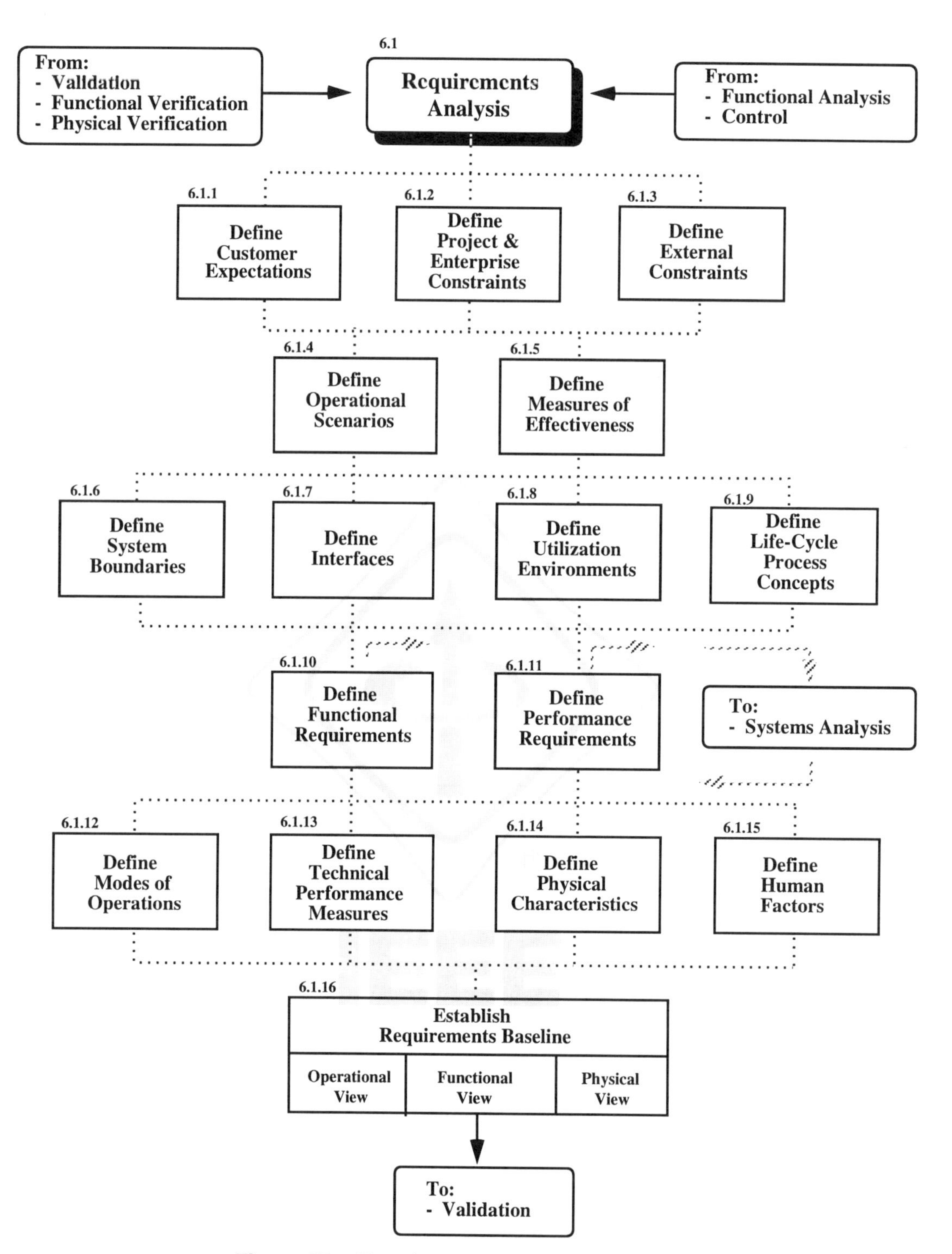

Figure 15— Requirements analysis process

6.1.16 Requirements baseline

The output of tasks 6.1.1 through 6.1.15 are recorded in three views (operational, functional, and physical) to form a requirements baseline that establishes the technical problem to be solved by the performing activity. The operational view describes how the system products will serve their users. It establishes how well and under what conditions the system products are to be used. The functional view describes what the system products must do to produce the desired behavior described in the operational view and provides a description of the methodology used to develop the view and decision rationale. The physical view describes the physical considerations of the system products development and establishes requirements for technologies and for physical interfaces among equipment and among operators and equipment. The content of these views may include the following:

a) Operational view
   1) Operational need description
   2) Results of system operational analyses
   3) Operational sequences/scenarios (best portrayed in pictures) that include utilization environments, MOEs, and how the system products will be used
   4) Conditions/events to which system products must respond
   5) Operational constraints including MOEs
   6) Identified user roles including job tasks and skill requirements
   7) Life cycle process concepts to include MOEs, critical MOPs, and already existing products and services
   8) Operational interfaces with other systems, platforms, and/or products
   9) System boundaries
b) Functional view
   1) Functional requirements that describe what system products and life cycle processes must do or accomplish
   2) Performance requirements including qualitative (how well), quantitative (how much, capacity), and time lines or periodicity (how long, how often) requirements
   3) Functional sequences for accomplishing system objectives
   4) Technical performance measurement criteria
   5) Functional interface requirements with external, higher-level, or interacting systems, platforms, and/or products
   6) Modes of operations
   7) Functional capabilities for planned evolutionary growth
c) Physical view
   1) Previously approved specifications and baselines
   2) Physical interfaces with other systems, platforms and/or products
   3) Human factors including skills required to accomplish functions of the system, and characteristics of information displays and operator controls
   4) Characterization of operator(s) and maintainers including special physical environments and applicable movement or visual limitations
   5) System characteristics including physical limitations (capacity, power, size, weight), technology limitations (precision, data rates, frequency, language), and standardized end items, nondevelopmental items, and reusability requirements
   6) Design constraints, including project, enterprise, and external constraints that limit physical solutions and/or development procedures
   7) Physical capabilities and capacities for planned evolutionary growth

6.2 Requirements validation

The performing activity shall perform a validation of the requirements baseline established during requirements analysis, in accordance with the following subclauses. Validation consists of two types of activities:

a) Evaluation of the requirements baseline to ensure that it represents identified customer expectations and project, enterprise, and external constraints.
b) Assessment of the requirements baseline to determine whether the full spectrum of possible system operations and system life cycle support concepts has been adequately addressed.

When voids in needs, constraints, etc. are identified or needs are not properly addressed, requirements analysis and validation are repeated until a valid requirements baseline is generated. The validated requirements baseline is documented in the integrated database and is an input to functional analysis. The tasks associated with validation are identified in figure 16.

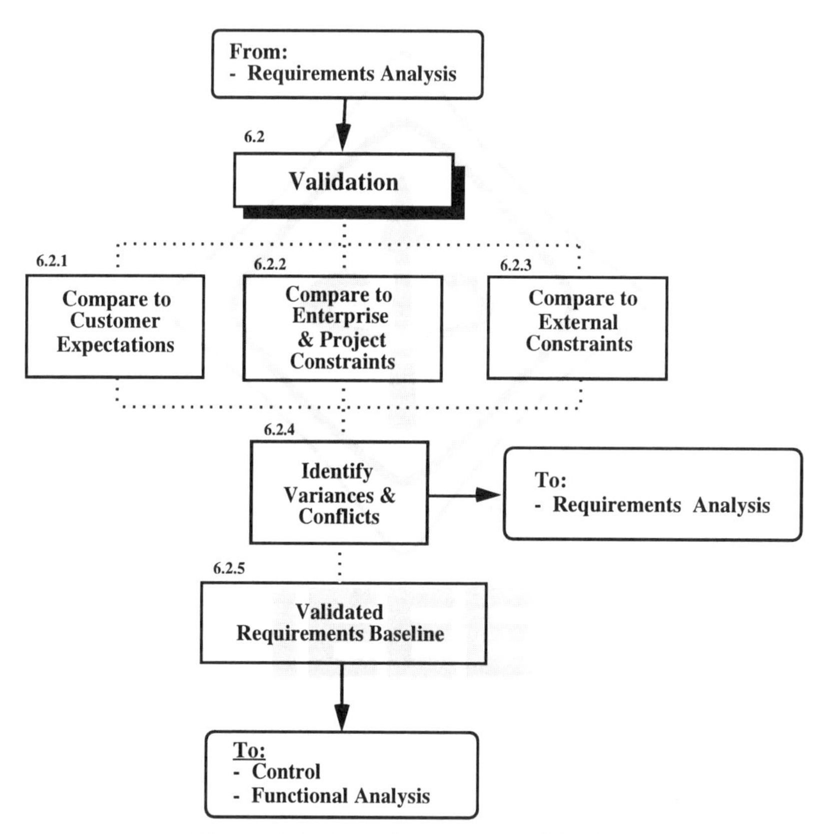

Figure 16—Requirements validation

6.2.1 Customer expectations

The performing activity analyzes and compares the established requirements baseline against customer expectations to ensure that the technical requirements adequately represent the customer's needs, requirements, and constraints for system products and life cycle support concepts. This involves direct customer involvement (end-user, marketing, etc.) and/or customer-provided requirement documents.

6.2.2 Enterprise and project constraints

The performing activity analyzes and compares the established requirements baseline against enterprise and project constraints to ensure that the technical requirements correctly represent and stay within enterprise and project policies and procedures, acceptable risk levels, plans, resources, technology limitations, objectives, decisions, standards, or other documented constraints.

6.2.3 External constraints

The performing activity analyzes and compares the established requirements baseline against external constraints to ensure that the specified technical requirements correctly represent and stay within applicable national and international laws (including environmental protection, hazardous material exclusion lists, waste handling, and social responsibility laws); correctly state external interface requirements with existing or evolving systems, platforms, or products; include applicable general specification and standard provisions affecting the development; and adequately define competitive product capabilities and characteristics.

6.2.4 Variances and conflicts

The performing activity identifies and defines variances and conflicts that arise out of the validation tasks in 6.2.1 through 6.2.3. Each variance or conflict must be resolved by iterating through requirements analysis to refine the requirements baseline.

6.2.5 Validated requirements baseline

Once the established requirements baseline variations and conflicts are satisfactorily resolved, the requirements baseline is considered valid. This validated requirements baseline is then used as input to functional analysis (see 6.3) and documented in the integrated database.

6.3 Functional analysis

The performing activity shall perform functional analysis, in accordance with the following subclauses, to describe the problem defined by requirements analysis in clearer detail. This is accomplished by translating the validated requirements baseline into a functional architecture. The functional architecture describes the functional arrangements and sequencing of subfunctions resulting from decomposing (breaking down) the set of system functions to their subfunctions. Functional analysis should be performed without consideration for a design solution. Groups of subfunctions generated during functional analysis set the criteria that will guide the definition of product and subsystem solutions during synthesis (see 6.5). The tasks of functional analysis are identified in figure 17.

6.3.1 Functional decomposition

The performing activity decomposes system functions identified in the validated requirements baseline into subfunctions with the intent of defining alternative subfunction arrangements and sequences, their functional interfaces, and their performance requirements. The extent of decomposition depends on establishing a clear understanding of what the system must accomplish. Generally, one level of decomposition is sufficient. Trade studies and risk analyses (see 6.7) are performed to select a balanced set of subfunctions (no one subfunction is optimized at the expense of another subfunction, an arrangement of subfunctions, or interacting interface), and to allocate performance requirements to subfunctions to assure requirements are balanced across subfunctions and to resolve conflicts among allocated performance requirements and nonallocable requirements.

6.3.1.1 Subfunctions

Subfunctions are defined in terms of their functional behaviors, states and modes of operation, functional time lines, conditions for control or data flow, functional failure modes and effects, and potential hazard monitoring functions that will be needed. Alternative arrangements and sequencing of subfunctions are explored to assure a balanced set of subfunctions to analyze, define, and structure the functional architecture. Arrangements can be by logical groupings, functional flows, time ordering, data flow, control flow, or some other method. The performing activity analyzes resulting subfunction arrangements to determine the degree of redundancy. Identified redundant functions, not specifically needed for safety, reliability, or other critical requirement, should be eliminated. The performing activity selects the best subfunction arrangement and documents it in the integrated database.

6.3.1.2 Functional interfaces

As system functions are decomposed into subfunctions, interfaces between interacting subfunctions are created. The performing activity identifies these interfaces and defines their functional interactions such as start and end states or inputs and outputs.

6.3.1.3 Performance requirements

Performance requirements in the validated requirements baseline are divided into allocable and nonallocable requirements. Allocable requirements are progressively divided to lower levels. Allocable requirements are directly or indirectly allocated to subfunctions. Directly allocable requirements such as time to perform or weight, are partitioned among subfunctions, as appropriate. Requirements that are not directly allocable, such as range, must be translated into derived performance requirements such as fuel capacity, engine efficiency, and vehicle resistance through appropriate engineering techniques and analyses. Nonallocable requirements are applied directly to all subfunctions (e.g., constraint, material or process standard). The performing activity documents the allocation of system performance requirements to subfunctions to provide traceability and facilitate later changes.

6.3.2 Functional behaviors

The performing activity analyzes each subfunction and aggregate of subfunctions to determine the responses (output) of the function(s) to stimuli (inputs). Analyses are conducted to understand the functional behavior of subfunctions under various conditions and check the integrity of the functional arrangement logic. Analyses should involve the simulation or stimulation of functional models, utilizing operational scenarios that expose the model to a variety of stressful and nonstressful situations that reflect anticipated operational usage and environments.

6.3.3 Subfunction states and modes

The performing activity analyzes each subfunction, and aggregate of subfunctions, to identify and define the states and modes for which subfunctions exhibit different behaviors. The analyses include state or mode transitions between start and end conditions of a subfunction, or aggregate of subfunctions.

6.3.4 Functional time line

The performing activity analyzes sequences of subfunctions and their behaviors to identify and define a functional time line for each operational scenario. The ranges for the execution time for each subfunction and the conditions that cause normal and abnominal performance are identified in support of each functional time line.

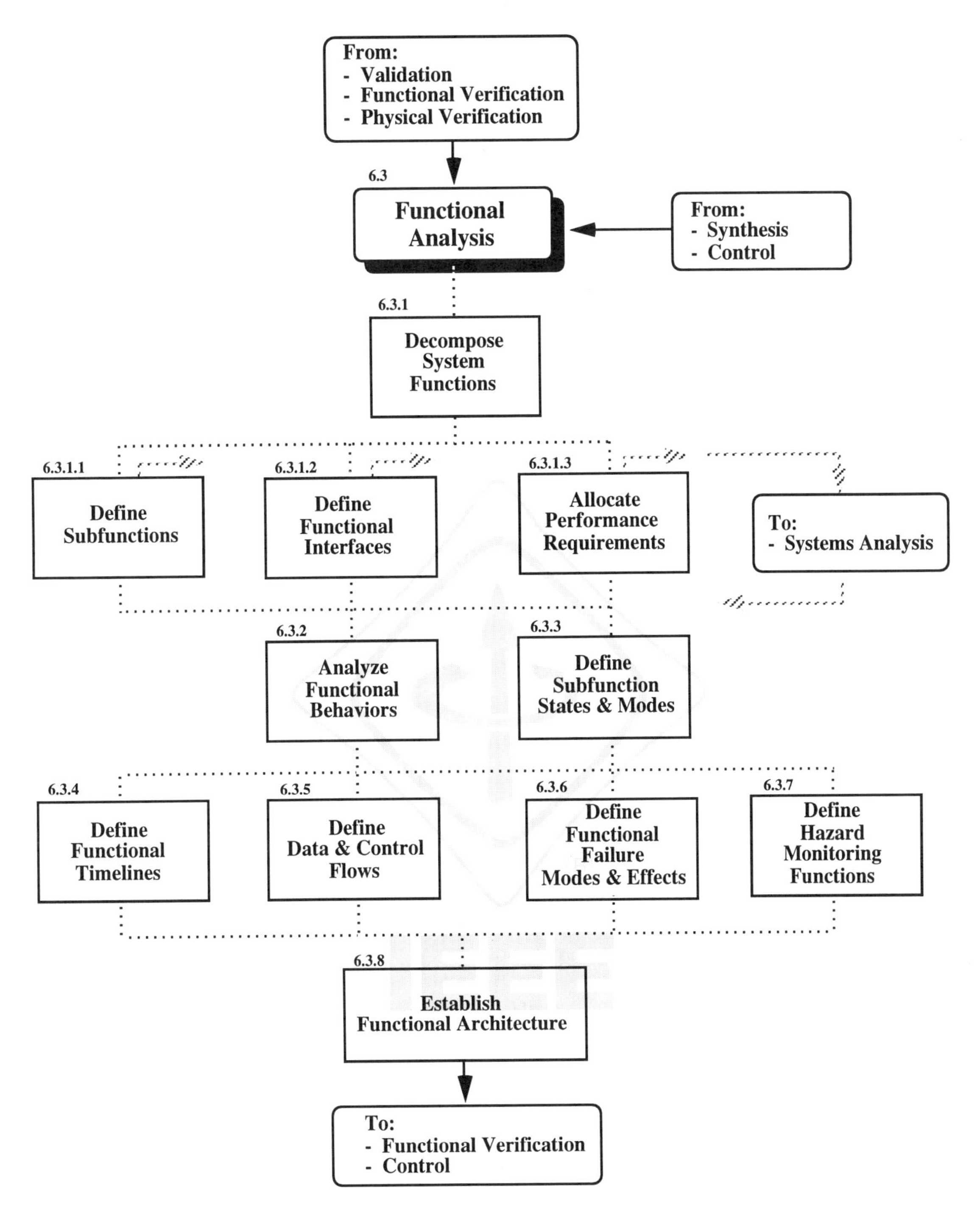

Figure 17—Functional analysis process

6.3.5 Data and control flows

The performing activity analyzes sequences of subfunctions and their behaviors to identify and define data flows among the subfunctions for each operational scenario. These data flows are captured in a data flow diagram. The functional execution controls of each subfunction, and among subfunctions, are identified and defined for each operational scenario and captured in a control-flow diagram.

6.3.6 Functional failure modes and effects

The performing activity analyzes and prioritizes potential functional failure modes to define failure effects and identify the need for fault detection and recovery functions. Functional reliability models are established to support the analysis of system effectiveness for each operational scenario. Failures that represent significant safety, performance, or environmental hazards are modeled to completely understand system impacts.

6.3.7 Hazard monitoring functions

The performing activity analyzes subfunctions and aggregates of subfunctions to identify operational hazards that could result in personal injury, property or product damage, or environmental impacts. Functional requirements for monitoring dangerous operational conditions, or notifying or warning operators of impending hazards, are defined.

6.3.8 Functional architecture

The performing activity establishes the functional architecture, appropriate to the level of development, to define lower-level functional and performance requirements from which and for which physical solutions will be determined in synthesis (see 6.5). Prior to synthesis, the functional architecture must be verified to assure that it meets the requirements of the validated requirements baseline.

6.4 Functional verification

The performing activity shall conduct the functional verification process, in accordance with the following subclauses, to assess the completeness of the functional architecture in satisfying the validated requirements baseline and produce a verified functional architecture for input to synthesis. The tasks that define functional verification are identified in figure 18.

6.4.1 Verification procedures

The performing activity defines the procedures for verifying the established functional architecture.

6.4.2 Verification evaluation

The performing activity conducts defined procedures to verify that each requirement and constraint described by the established functional architecture is upward traceable to the validated requirements baseline and that all top-level system requirements and constraints recorded in the requirements baseline are downward traceable to the functional architecture.

6.4.2.1 Architecture completeness

The performing activity verifies that all top-level system product operational requirements included in the requirements baseline are traceable to the functional architecture.

6.4.2.2 Functional and performance measures

The performing activity verifies that all system-level functional and performance requirements of the requirements baseline are traceable to the established functional architecture.

6.4.2.3 Satisfaction of constraints

The performing activity verifies that all system-level policy and procedural, standardization, functional, and physical constraints of the requirements baseline are traceable to the established functional architecture.

6.4.3 Variances and conflicts

The performing activity identifies voids, variances, and conflicts resulting from verification evaluation activities task in 6.4.2. When incompleteness is shown, functional analysis tasks (see 6.3) are repeated to correct voids. When functional architecture requirements are not upward traceable to the validated requirements baseline, it must be determined if non required functions and/or performance requirements were introduced during functional analysis, or whether valid functional and/or performance requirements were introduced and need to be reflected in the requirements baseline. The former requires that functional analysis (see 6.3) be repeated to eliminate non required functions and/or performance requirements. For the latter variance or conflict, requirements analysis (see 6.1) and validation (see 6.2) must be repeated to produce a new validated requirements baseline.

6.4.4 Verified functional architecture

The functional architecture is verified upon satisfactorily completing the tasks in 6.4.2. The verified functional architecture, with rationale justifying the structure, trade studies performed, and key decisions, is documented in the integrated database. This verified functional architecture is used in synthesis to generate physical solutions to satisfy customer expectations and meet public acceptance as defined by the validated requirements baseline.

6.5 Synthesis

The performing activity shall perform synthesis, in accordance with the following subclauses, for the purpose of defining system product solutions and identifying subsystems to satisfy the requirements of the verified functional architecture. Synthesis translates the functional architecture into a physical architecture that provides an arrangement of elements, their decomposition, interfaces (internal and external), physical constraints, and designs. The activities of tasks in 6.5.1 through 6.5.14 involve selecting a preferred solution or arrangement from a set of alternatives and understanding associated cost, schedule, performance, and risk implications. Systems analysis (see 6.7) is used as necessary to aid alternative selections; to identify, assess, and quantify risks, and select proper handling approaches; and to understand cost, schedule, and performance impacts. As subsystem requirements are defined, the identification of the needs, requirements, and constraints for life cycle processes is completed.

6.5.1 Group and allocate functions

The performing activity groups or partitions the functions and subfunctions of the verified functional architecture into logical physical elements representing system products or their subsystems (see 1.3). A function or set of subfunctions can be assigned to more than one physical element. Requirements traceability is established and recorded to ensure that all functions of the functional architecture are allocated to a physical element; and physical elements perform at least one function.

6.5.2 Physical solution alternatives

The performing activity generates alternative solutions for the physical elements identified in 6.5.1. These solutions will be composed of one or more of the following—hardware, software, material, data, facility, people, services, and techniques. As tasks in 6.5.3 through 6.5.14 are completed, alternatives and aggregates of alternatives are analyzed to determine which best satisfies allocated functional and performance requirements, derived and interface requirements, and design constraints; and adds to the overall effectiveness of the system or higher-level system. As these tasks are completed, specialty engineers work with design engineers to ensure requirements such as reliability, availability, maintainability, safety, health factors, security, survivability, electromagnetic compatibility, radio frequency management, human factors are designed in as appropriate. Additionally, life cycle process requirements are identified and defined for each alternative system product solution and aggregate of solutions.

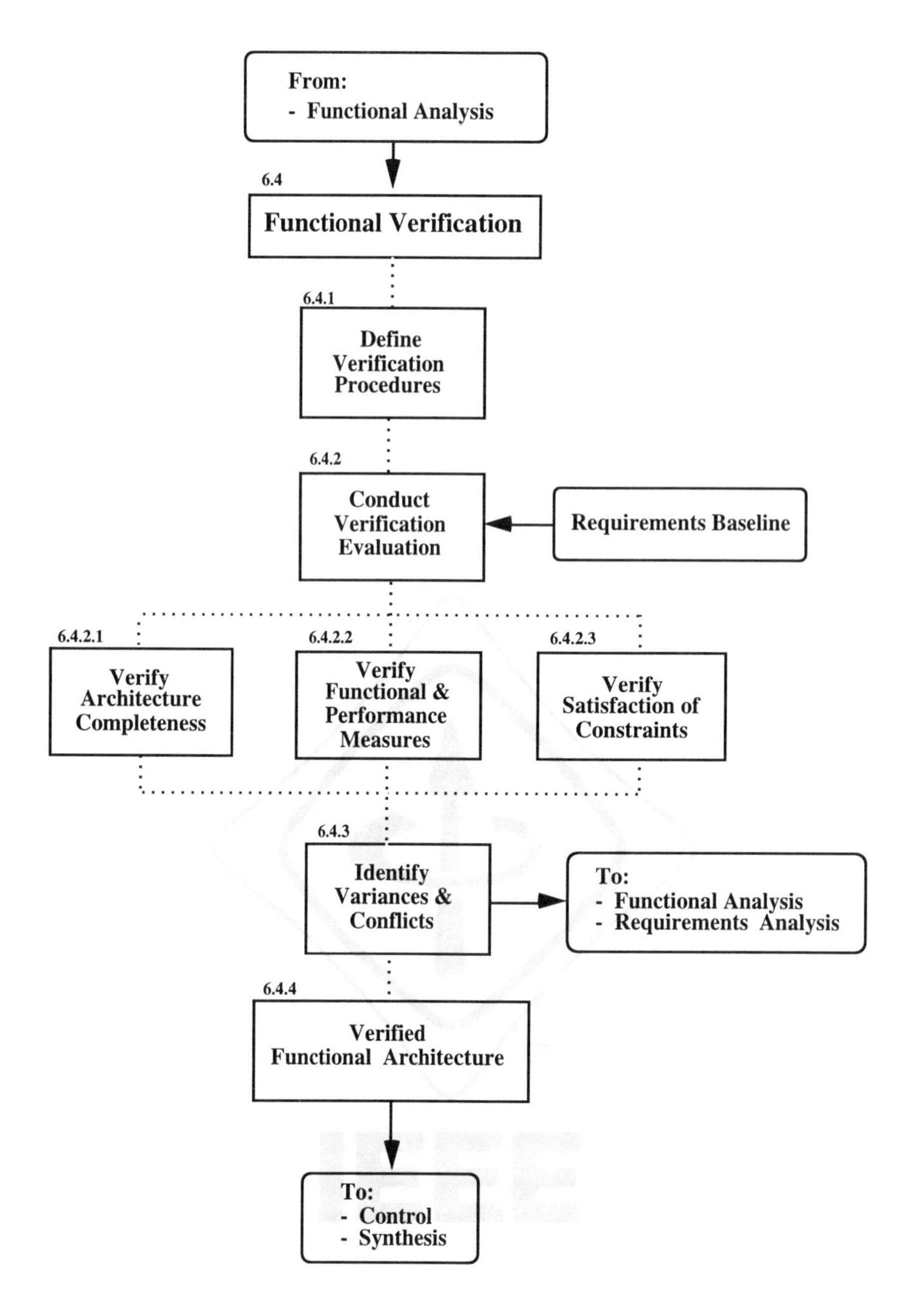

Figure 18—Functional verification

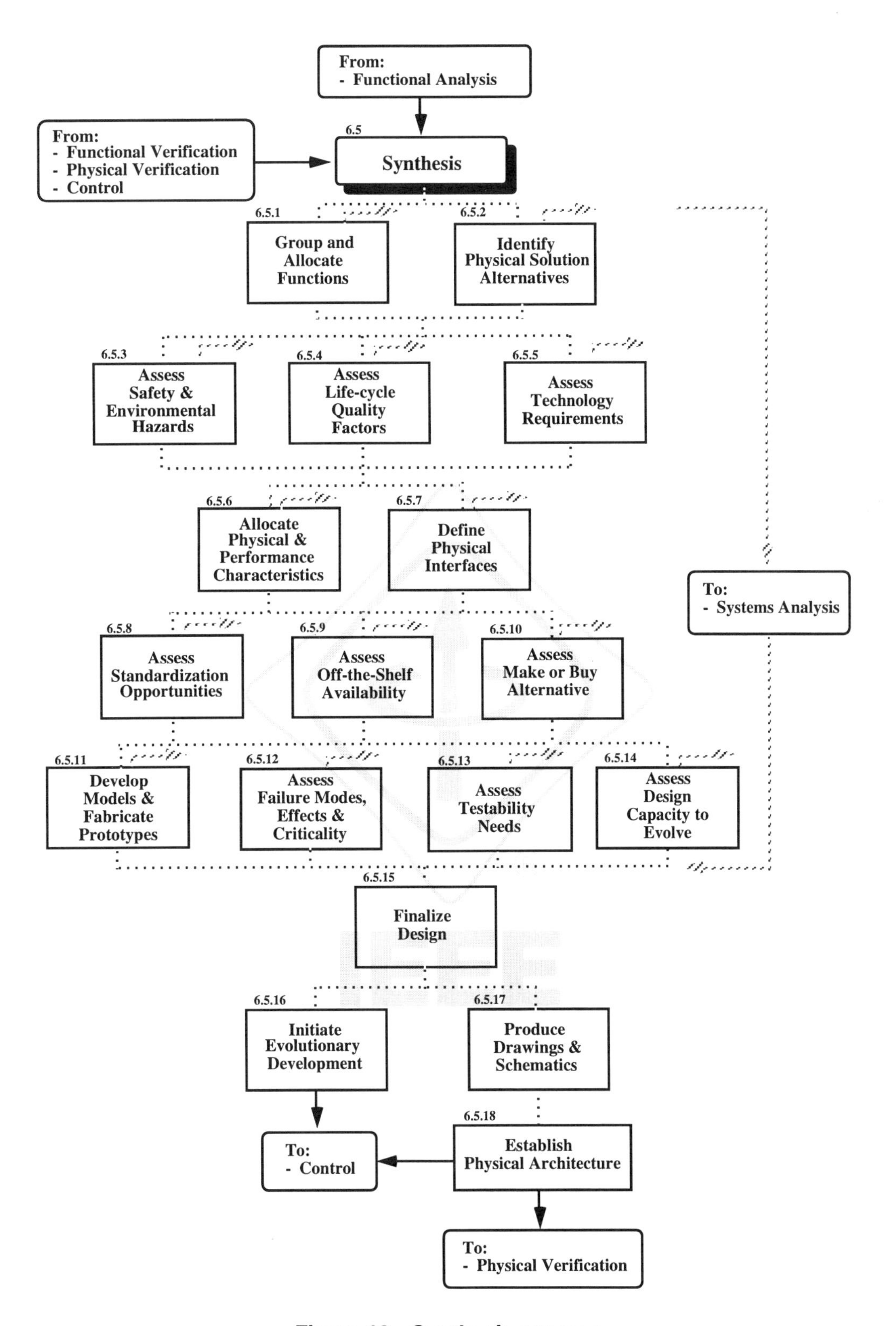

Figure 19—Synthesis process

6.5.3 Safety and environmental hazards

The performing activity analyzes alternatives of 6.5.2 and aggregates of alternatives to identify potential hazards to the system, its operators, or the environment. Special attention is placed on assessing safe operations of the system and assessing pollutants, hazardous wastes, or by-products associated with manufacturing, test, distribution, operation, support, training, or disposal of the system as developed to date.

6.5.4 Life cycle quality factors

The performing activity assesses alternatives of 6.5.2 to determine the degree to which quality factors (producibility, testability, ease of distribution, operability, supportability, trainability, and disposability) have been included in the solutions. Additionally, the performing activity assesses whether associated life cycle process needs, requirements, and constraints of the processes are identified and defined.

6.5.5 Technology requirements

The performing activity assesses alternatives of 6.5.2 to determine the technological needs necessary to make the physical solution effective. The risks associated with the introduction of any new or advanced technologies to meet requirements must be identified and assessed.

6.5.6 Physical and performance characteristics

The performing activity identifies and documents the physical and performance characteristics of alternatives of 6.5.2. The physical characteristics and human factors associated with life cycle quality factors should be identified and assessed.

6.5.7 Physical interfaces

The performing activity identifies and defines the physical interfaces among products, subsystems, life cycle processes, and external interfaces to higher-level systems or interacting systems. Physical interfaces that impact design include communication, data, support, test, connectivity, or resource replenishment characteristics of the interaction among subsystems, the products, or other interfacing systems or a higher-level system.

6.5.8 Standardization opportunities

The performing activity analyzes alternatives of 6.5.2 to assess whether use of standardized end items would be technologically and economically feasible.

6.5.9 Off-the-shelf availability

The performing activity analyzes alternatives of 6.5.2 to determine availability of an off-the-shelf end item (e.g., nondevelopmental hardware or reusable software). Each identified off-the-shelf end item must be assessed to determine cost effectiveness, quantity, availability, and viability of the supplier and/or their product.

6.5.10 Make or buy alternatives

The performing activity performs an economic analysis on alternatives of 6.5.2 to support make or buy decisions. This analysis should address whether it is more cost effective for the enterprise to produce the physical element versus going to an established supplier.

6.5.11 Models and prototypes

The performing activity develops models and/or prototypes to

a) Assist in identifying and reducing risks associated with integrating available and emerging technologies
b) Verify that the physical solution (made up of hardware, software, material, humans, facilities, techniques, data, and/or service) meets allocated functional and performance requirements, interface requirements, and constraints
c) Verify that the physical solution satisfies the functional architecture and requirements baseline.

The models, data files, and supporting documentation should be maintained, and each version of a model or data file that impacts requirements, designs, or decisions should be saved in the integrated database. Models may be digital, partial, or complete and may be hardware, software or a combination of both.

6.5.12 Failure modes, effects, and criticality.

The performing activity assesses failure modes, the effects, and the criticality of failure for alternatives of 6.5.2. The physical solution should be analyzed and historical or test data should be applied to refine an estimate of the probability of successful performance of each alternative. A Failure Modes and Effects Analysis (FMEA) should be used to identify the strengths and weaknesses of the physical solution. For critical failures, the performing activity conducts a criticality analysis to prioritize each alternative by its criticality rating. The results of this analysis are used to direct further design efforts to accommodate redundancy and to support graceful system degradation.

6.5.13 Testability needs

The performing activity assesses the testability of alternatives of 6.5.2 to determine Built-In Test (BIT) and/or Fault-Isolation Test (FIT) requirements to support operational or maintenance considerations. BIT-FIT mechanisms should be provided for those elements that are normally maintained by the operators, customer, or field support engineers. BIT-FIT can be used for diagnostic operations to support lower-level maintenance actions.

6.5.14 Design capacity to evolve

The performing activity assesses alternatives of 6.5.2 to determine the capacity of the physical solution to evolve, or be re-engineered, to accommodate new technologies, enhance performance, increase functionality, or other cost-effective or competitive improvements once the system is in production or in the marketplace. Limitations that may preclude the ability of a system to evolve should be identified and approaches analyzed and defined for resolving limitations. The performing activity must perform configuration management on products to ensure products that do have the capacity to evolve can be re-engineered cost effectively.

6.5.15 Design

The performing activity selects the physical solution assessed and defined in 6.5.2 through 6.5.14 for which design will be finalized. The designation and description of physical interfaces (internal and external) among physical elements are finalized.

6.5.16 Evolutionary development

The performing activity initiates an evolutionary development for any physical element of the finalized design for which a lesser technology solution was selected over a higher risk technology, and for which the capacity to evolve was designed in the physical element and interfacing elements.

6.5.17 Drawings and schematics

The performing activity completes all design activities to describe the selected physical elements. The finalized design includes all hardware drawings and schematics, software design documentation and source code listings, and interface descriptions.

6.5.18 Physical architecture

The performing activity establishes the physical architecture, appropriate to the level of development, to document the design solutions and interfaces determined by tasks in 6.5.1 through 6.5.16. The physical architecture includes the requirements traceability and allocation matrices that capture the allocation of functional and performance requirements among the system elements. Physical architecture definitions should be stored in the integrated database with all trade studies, design rationale, and key decisions to provide traceability of requirements up and down the architecture. Verification of the physical architecture (see 6.6) must be accomplished to demonstrate that the architecture meets the requirements of both the validated requirements baseline and the verified functional architecture.

6.6 Physical verification

The performing activity shall perform physical verification, in accordance with the following subclauses, for the purpose of

a) Assuring that the requirements of the lowest level of the physical architecture, including derived requirements, are traceable to the verified functional architecture
b) Assuring that the physical architecture requirements satisfy the validated requirements baseline

The physical verification tasks are identified in figure 20.

6.6.1 Verification approach

The performing activity accomplishes the tasks of 6.6.1.1 through 6.6.1.3 to select the approaches for verifying the physical architecture and the scenarios for assessing design completeness.

6.6.1.1 Inspection, analysis, demonstration, or test requirements

The performing activity selects the appropriate verification method (inspection, analysis—including simulation, demonstration, or test) for evaluating whether functional and performance requirements, and physical characteristic identified in the system baseline are satisfied by the physical architecture. A verification matrix is developed to trace the verification method(s) to requirements of the functional architecture and requirements baseline. The performing activity also selects the models or prototypes to be used, which may be partial or complete, depending on the purpose and objectives of the verification task.

6.6.1.2 Verification procedures

The performing activity defines procedures for each verification method selected, identifies the purpose and objectives of each verification procedure as well as the pre-test and post-test actions, and defines the criteria for determining the success or failure of the procedure for planned and abnormal conditions.

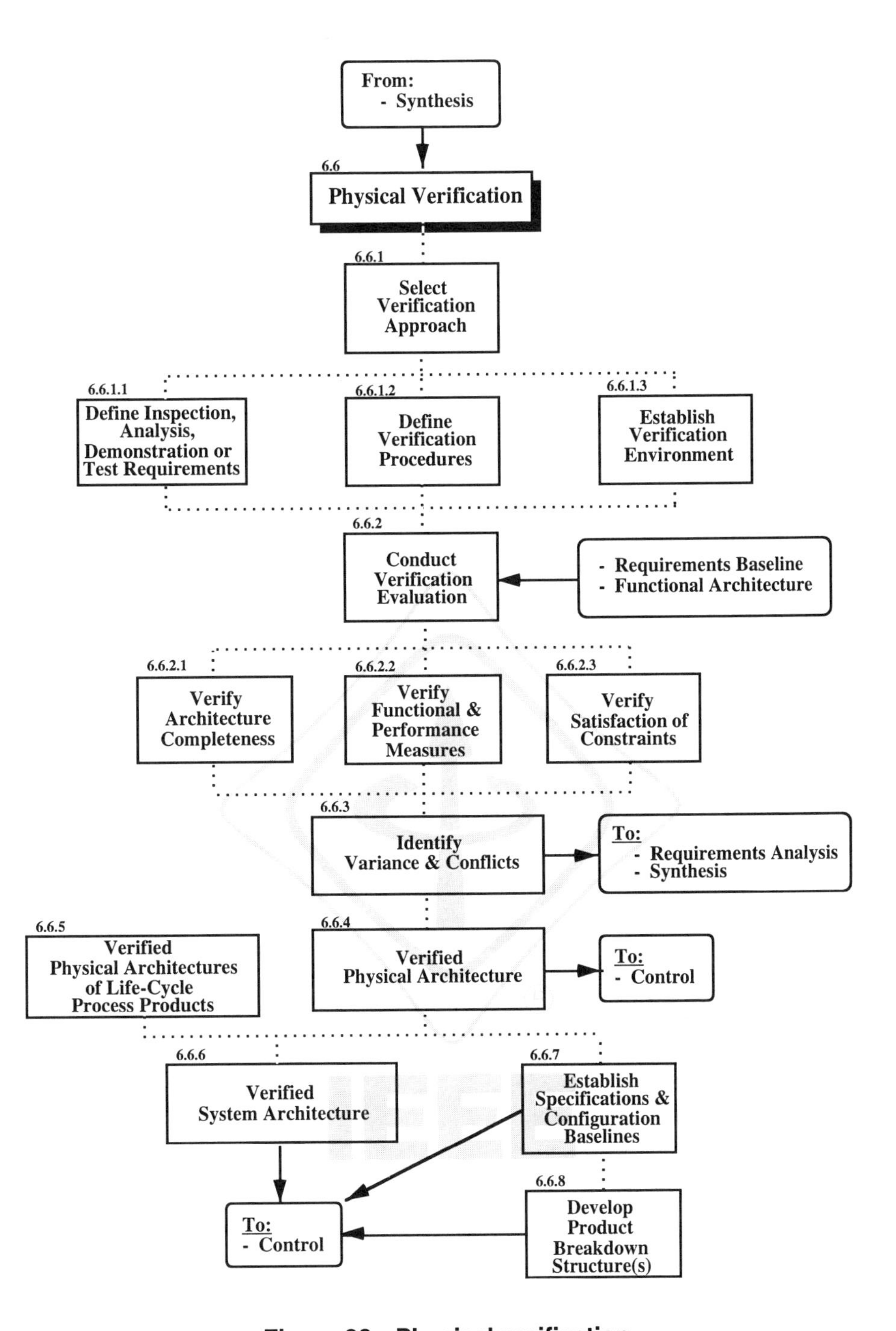

Figure 20—Physical verification

6.6.1.3 Verification environment

The performing activity establishes the environment for methods selected and procedures defined. Environment considerations include facilities, equipment, tools, simulations, measuring devices, personnel, and climatic conditions. Environment should be checked-out prior to conducting verification.

6.6.2 Verification evaluation

The performing activity conducts the tasks of 6.6.2.1 through 6.6.2.3 to verify that each requirement and constraint is traceable to the verified functional architecture and that the physical element solutions satisfy the validated requirements baseline. The verification results are evaluated to ensure that the behavior exhibited by the physical element solutions was anticipated and satisfies requirements.

6.6.2.1 Architecture completeness

The performing activity verifies that physical elements descriptions are traceable to requirements of the functional architecture (upward traceability), and the requirements of the functional architecture are allocated and traceable to the physical architecture. All internal and external physical interfaces must be upward and downward traceable to their source requirement.

6.6.2.2 Functional and performance measures

The performing activity verifies that the evaluations results from activities defined in 6.6.1 satisfy the functional and performance requirements of the validated requirements baseline.

6.6.2.3 Satisfaction of constraints

The performing activity verifies that the evaluation results from activities as defined in 6.6.1 satisfy the constraints, including interfaces, of the functional architecture, and the constraints of the established physical architecture are traceable to the validated requirements baseline.

6.6.3 Variances and conflicts

The performing activity identifies variances and conflicts resulting from verifying activities of tasks in 6.6.2. When variances show incompleteness, synthesis tasks (see 6.5) or functional analyses tasks in 6.3 are repeated to correct omissions. When evaluation results do not verify functional architecture requirements or when physical architecture requirements are not traceable to the functional architecture, it must be determined if nonrequired functions and/or performance requirements or physical elements were introduced during synthesis, or whether valid functional and/or performance requirements were introduced and need to be reflected in the functional architecture. The former requires that synthesis (see 6.5) be repeated to eliminate nonrequired functions and/or performance requirements. For the latter variance or conflict, requirements analysis through functional verification (see 6.1 through 6.4) must be repeated to produce a new validated requirements baseline and verified functional architecture. When physical architecture requirements are not traceable to the validated requirements baseline, it may require that synthesis be repeated to eliminate nonrequired functional and or performance requirements; or it may require that the systems engineering process activities be repeated, as necessary, to include those missing requirements.

6.6.4 Verified physical architecture

The physical architecture is verified upon satisfactorily completing the physical verification task of 6.6.2. The verified physical architecture, with rationale justifying the structure, trade studies performed, and key decisions, is documented in the integrated database. This verified physical architecture is used to form the specification tree for the system and, when combined with the verified life cycle process physical architectures, forms the system architecture.

6.6.5 Verified life cycle process physical architectures

The performing activity completes requirements analysis, functional analysis, and synthesis tasks to identify, define, and design physical architectures for life cycle processes. The performing activity performs the tasks of 6.1 through 6.4 to verify the physical architecture for each life cycle process product. The products associated with each life cycle process are bought or made, and integrated with other products related to the process or other processes, in a timely manner to support key project events.

6.6.6 Verified system architecture

A complete system architecture is composed of all life cycle process physical architectures and consumer product physical architectures. The system architecture is verified upon satisfactorily completing the verification of the consumer products and their life cycle process products.

6.6.7 Establish specifications and configuration baselines

After verification of the physical architecture, the performing activity develops/updates product and interface specifications appropriate to the stage of development (see clause 4) for each element of the physical architecture. In addition, the performing activity develops/updates appropriate configuration baselines for each element of the physical architecture. The hierarchy of specifications (product and interface) for the physical architecture forms the specification tree appropriate for the stage of development (see figure 6). The specification tree delineates specification elements for which a product must be fabricated, manufactured, bought, or coded. Specifications are stored in the integrated database and used in the next application of the systems engineering process. The design solution for the next level of development must satisfy these specifications.

6.6.8 Develop system breakdown structure

The performing activity develops a system breakdown structure (SBS) from the specification tree for the system designed, including life cycle process requirements (see figure 7), by tasks 6.5.1 through 6.5.17. The SBS is stored in the integrated database and is used to structure and manage technical activities of the next stage of development.

6.7 Systems analysis

The performing activity shall perform systems analyses, in accordance with the following subclauses, for the purpose of resolving conflicts identified during requirements analysis, decomposing functional requirements and allocating performance requirements during functional analysis, evaluating the effectiveness of alternative physical element solutions and selecting the best physical solution during synthesis, assessing system effectiveness, and managing risk factors throughout the systems engineering effort. Systems analyses provides a rigorous quantitative basis for establishing a balanced set of requirements and for ending up with a balanced design. The tasks of systems analysis are identified in figure 21. Even if a trade study is not done, an overall assessment of the system effectiveness shall be completed.

6.7.1 Requirement conflicts

The performing activity assesses conflicts among requirements and constraints identified during requirements analysis to identify alternative functional and performance requirements, where necessary. Conflicts may be between functional requirements, performance requirements, or constraints, or between combinations of these. Requirements trade studies and assessments are performed to identify the recommended set of requirements and constraints in terms of risk, cost, schedule, and performance impacts.

6.7.2 Functional alternatives

The performing activity assesses possible alternative subfunction arrangements for the decomposition of a function and for the allocation of allocable performance requirements to the subfunctions during functional analysis. Functional trade studies and assessments are performed to identify the recommended set of subfunctions for each function and performance requirement allocations in terms of risk, cost, schedule, and performance impacts.

6.7.3 Solution alternatives

The performing activity assesses potential groupings and allocations of functions from the verified functional architecture and identified physical solution alternatives during synthesis. Design trade studies and assessments are performed to identify the recommended design solution trade-offs in terms of risk, cost, schedule, and performance impacts.

6.7.4 Risk factors (identify)

The performing activity assesses requirements and constraints from requirements analysis, subfunction arrangements resulting from functional decomposition, allocation of subfunctions to logical physical elements, each design decision made during synthesis, and each physical element of the physical architecture to identify things that can go wrong, such as the risk factors. These evaluations should be made from an entire life cycle perspective. Identification of risk should be in a form to understand:

a) The circumstances that might lead to risk factor occurrence and the probability of occurrence
b) How the risk factor can be recognized, if it does occur
c) How the risk factor will affect cost, schedule, and performance

Identified risks are prioritized based upon criticality to the successful development of the system. Acceptable levels of risk should be identified, depending on the stage of development, to provide a basis for establishing and monitoring risk-reduction activities and mitigating unacceptable risks.

6.7.5 Trade study scope

The performing activity completes tasks in 6.7.5.1 through 6.7.5.3 to define the scope of the trade study to be conducted. A trade study can be

a) *Judgemental.* A selection made based on the judgment of the analyst or designer that does not require the rigor of a more formal study and for which the consequences are not too important. One alternative is clearly superior to others, and/or time may not be available for a more formal approach (most trade studies done in accomplishing the tasks of the systems engineering process are of the mental type).
b) *Informal.* Follows the same methodology of a formal trade study but is not documented as formally and is of less importance to the customer.
c) *Formal.* Formally conducted with results reviewed at technical reviews.

Informal and formal trade study objectives, execution, data collection requirements, schedule of activities, analysis of results, and expected outcomes need to be fully defined. Each trade study is conducted for the purpose of selecting between competing alternatives to support customer needs, system effectiveness, design-to-cost, or life cycle cost objectives within acceptable levels of risk.

6.7.5.1 Methodology and success criteria

The performing activity selects the general approach, resources, and procedures for performing trade studies based upon the trade-study definition, its level of importance, and availability of tools, facilities, special equipment, and related resources. The performing activity also lists the set of selection criteria that includes factors that characterize what makes a specific alternative desirable, such as cost, schedule, performance, and risk; life cycle quality factors; reuse; and size, weight, and power consumption. Adverse qualities as well as favorable qualities should be included as criteria.

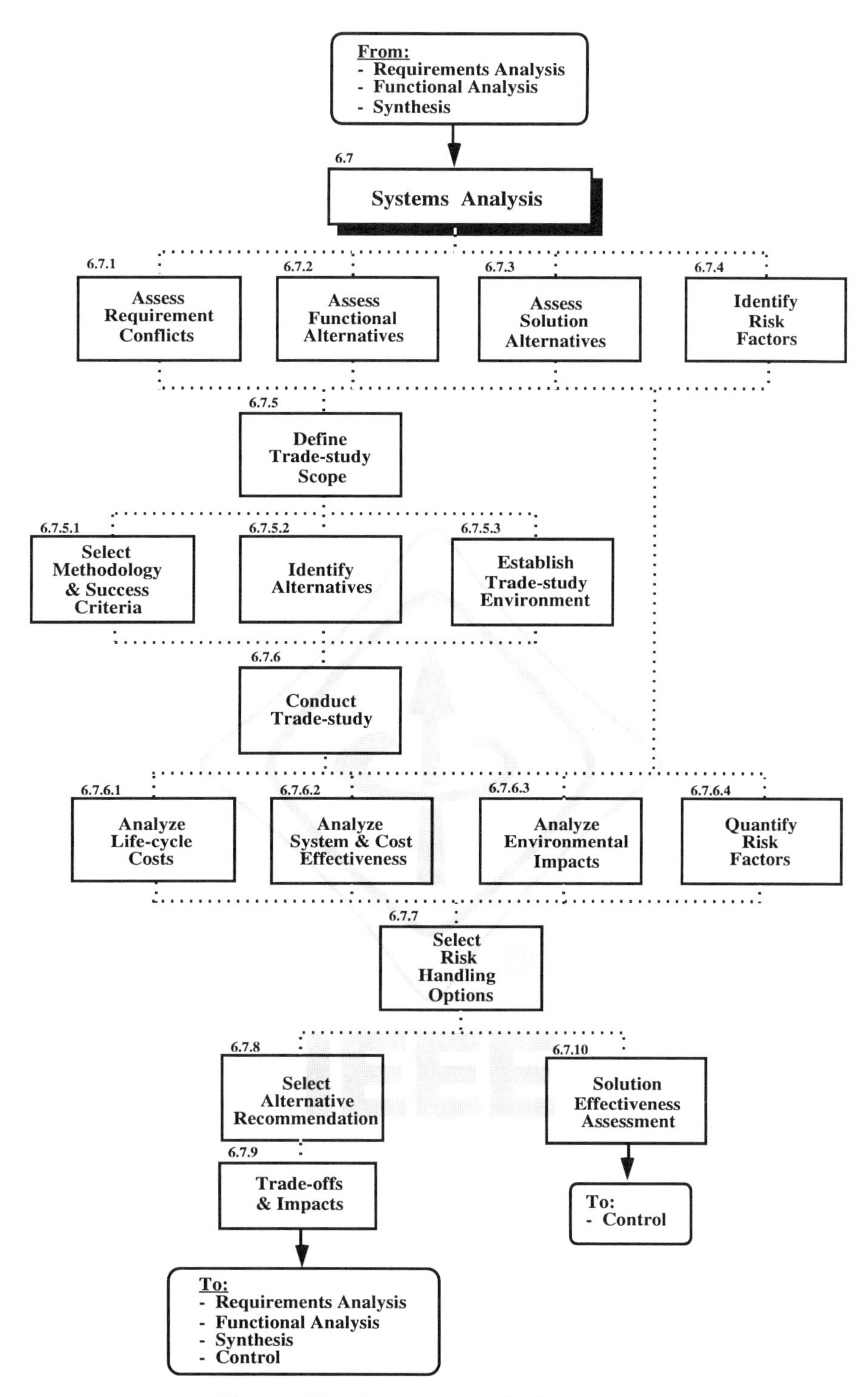

Figure 21— Systems analysis process

6.7.5.2 Alternatives

The performing activity identifies and lists the viable alternative solutions to be evaluated. When feasible, each alternative should be comparable with respect to completeness. When not feasible, selection criteria and weighting values will compensate for the disparity.

6.7.5.3 Trade-study environment

The performing activity establishes metrics for each criterion that characterizes how well various alternatives satisfy the criterion. In addition, the performing activity establishes weighting factors for each criteria that distinguish the degree of importance to the trade study definition. Models (representative or simulations) are established when needed to support conduct of a formal or informal trade study. The selection of models depends on the nature of the trade study, the development stage, the type of information needed, and the characteristics of interest for an alternative. Models must be validated prior to application in a trade study.

6.7.6 Trade study

The performing activity completes tasks in 6.7.6.1 through 6.7.6.4, to the degree appropriate, to complete trade studies for the following:

a) Requirements analysis to both resolve conflicts with and satisfy customer/market needs, requirements, and constraints
b) Functional analysis to support decomposition of functions into subfunctions and to allocate performance requirements
c) Synthesis to support design decisions

Formal and informal trade studies are conducted under controlled conditions to generate data pertaining to each alternative. The results of the trade studies are recorded and analyzed to quantify the impact each alternative has on the system or project. These results are compared against the success criteria to determine which alternative is recommended.

6.7.6.1 Life cycle costs

The performing activity analyzes the costs to the enterprise and to the customer for alternative system approaches considered in a trade study or system effectiveness assessment. Life cycle cost analyses

a) Provide requisite cost information to support trade-study decisions
b) Provide requisite cost information for system effectiveness assessments
c) Include the cost of development, manufacturing, test, distribution, operations, support, training, and disposal
d) Include established design-to-cost goals, a current estimate of these costs, and known uncertainties in these costs
e) Identify the impacts on life cycle cost of proposed changes

6.7.6.2 System and cost effectiveness

The performing activity analyzes the relationships between system effectiveness and life cycle costs to

a) Determine performance impacts on costs
b) Understand value added as a function of cost
c) Support identification of performance objectives and requirements
d) Support allocation of performance to functions

System and cost effectiveness analyses are conducted on life cycle processes of manufacturing, test, distribution, operations, support, training, and disposal to support inclusion of life cycle quality factors into system product designs and to support the definition of functional and performance requirements for life cycle processes. The results of these analyses are used in evaluating trade-study alternatives and for effectiveness assessments of the system.

6.7.6.3 Environmental impacts

The performing activity identifies all applicable environmental laws, regulations, and applicable hazardous material lists affecting the project and ensures that such are complied with by any alternative solution. The performing activity completes an environmental impact analysis to determine the impact on and by system products and their life cycle processes on the infrastructure; land and ocean; atmosphere; water sources; and human, animal, and plant life. Use of materials, or generating by-products, which present a known hazard to the environment, are to be avoided to the extent feasible. Where not feasible, provisions must be provided for proper handling, storage, and disposal of hazardous materials or by-products. Results of these analyses influence trade study recommendations and assessments of system effectiveness.

6.7.6.4 Risk factors (quantify)

The performing activity quantifies the impact of identified risk factors on the system or alternative being considered based on exposure to the probability of an undesirable consequence. For system effectiveness assessments, each element of the system architecture developed to date is assessed to determine what can go wrong and if it goes wrong what impact it will have on the system. For trade studies, risk levels assessed during life cycle cost, system and cost effectiveness, and environmental impact analyses are prioritized and reported as part of trade-study recommendations.

6.7.7 Risk handling option

The performing activity assesses various risk handling options to select those that will mitigate risks consistent with the current stage of development and risk management policies set by the project. Risk may be reduced by lessening either the likelihood or the impact, or both may be accepted given the cost, schedule, and performance impacts and planned mitigation approaches. An analysis of the risk handling options should be accomplished to quantify costs and effects on the probability and impact of risk. The performing activity should select those risk handling options that are feasible and that reduce risks to acceptable levels with the best cost/benefit ratio. The expected remaining risks after risk handling mitigation efforts are implemented should be identified and quantified. Throughout risk identification, quantification, and handling, integration is needed from lower levels of the system architecture up through the system level to understand cause and effect interactions. Risk reduction approaches and expected remaining risks are included in a risk reduction plan that is included in trade study recommendations and effectiveness assessment reports. The complete risk reduction effort is documented in the SEMP and integrated into the SEMS for the next stage of development and briefed at appropriate technical reviews.

6.7.8 Alternative recommendation

The performing activity utilizes the methods selected in the task in 6.7.5, the results from tasks in 6.7.6.1 through 6.7.6.4, and risk reduction planning information to recommend a preferred alternative to the decision maker. The performing activity should assess the trade study to assure that the methodologies and data collection instrumentation were sufficient to support a fair and complete evaluation. Each recommendation should be presented in terms of configuration and cost, schedule, performance, and risk impact.

6.7.9 Trade-offs and impacts

The performing activity documents the recommended trade-off alternative(s) with corresponding impacts and presents the results to the appropriate decision makers within the systems engineering process activity making or requesting the trade study. The final alternative selection is made based on the criteria established to judge a desirable solution. Key trade study activities, decisions, rationale, and recommendations are documented in the integrated database.

6.7.10 Solution effectiveness assessment

The performing activity determines the effectiveness of the current system solution based on the results of the assessments and analyses completed in the tasks in 6.7.3, 6.7.4, 6.7.6.1 through 6.7.6.4, and 6.7.7. The results of these assessments and analyses are documented in the integrated database and briefed at appropriate technical reviews and project reviews.

6.8 Control

The performing activity shall perform the tasks of control, in accordance with the following subclauses, for the purpose of managing and documenting the activities of the systems engineering process. The tasks of control are identified in figure 22. Outputs and activity reports from subprocess tasks in 6.1 through 6.7 and their test results, the planning for the conduct of the systems engineering process activities (SEMP, SEMS, and SEDS), and project technical plans generated by engineering specialties contributing to the activities of the systems engineering process are controlled by the performing activity. The control tasks provide

a) A complete and up-to-date picture of systems engineering process activities and results that are used in accomplishing other subprocess activities
b) Planning for and inputs to future applications of the systems engineering process
c) Information for production, test, and customer support
d) Information for decision makers at technical and project reviews

6.8.1 Design capture

The performing activity creates a process to capture all design data for control of activities within the systems engineering process and for re-engineering the system at a later time. The essential data are described in the tasks in 6.8.1.1 through 6.8.1.3.

6.8.1.1 Data and schema

The performing activity captures all design data from requirements analysis, validation, functional analysis, functional verification, synthesis, physical verification, and systems analysis. These data include the SEMP; SEMS; SEDS; technical plans; requirements baselines; functional, physical, and system architectures; rationale for design decisions; trade studies accomplished, including recommendations and impacts; effectiveness assessments and their outcomes; risk assessments and handling options; sketches and drawings; engineering changes; specification trees; specifications and configuration baselines; operational environment; archival data; technical objectives, requirements, constraints, interfaces, and risks; system breakdown structures; physical models; test results; metrics; and any other data that allows for traceability of requirements throughout the functional and physical architectures. Correlation matrixes are captured for work tasks and persons and/or organizations responsible for accomplishing the work, allocation of functions to logical physical elements, and trade study evaluation tables.

6.8.1.2 Tools

The performing activity captures the tools used to conduct and support requirements analysis, validation, functional analysis, functional verification, synthesis, physical verification, and systems analysis. Tools include systems engineering and software-automated tools and communication, reasoning, and knowledge-based, and status/projection tools. Traceability of tools used and results obtained should be captured.

6.8.1.3 Process models

The performing activity documents all representative and simulation models used for requirements analysis, validation, functional analysis, functional verification, synthesis, physical verification, systems analysis, controls, tests, and metrics development to assure the validity and integrity of the results and to provide a history of the application of models as the system evolves. Representations and simulations models may be made up of one or more of the following types—physical, graphical, mathematical (deterministic), and statistical. Model validation procedures and results are captured.

6.8.2 Technical management

The performing activity manages the tasks and activities of the systems engineering process by completing the tasks in 6.8.2.1 through 6.8.2.5 to control data generated, configuration of the physical solutions, interfaces, risks, and technical progress. The performing activity needs to maintain the correct staffing, facilities, equipment, and tools; manage costs and schedules; replan development activities, as required; coordinate technical interactions with customers; assure proper training of technical personnel and team members; measure technical progress; and coordinate the activities among the technical and business specialties needed to accomplish the systems engineering tasks of this standard.

6.8.2.1 Data management

The performing activity conducts data management to support the development, control, and delivery of required technical data throughout the project. Data management activities include setting up appropriate databases and procedures for capturing and retaining design data and schema, tools, and models. Data pertinent to the technical effort are readily accessible and should be maintained throughout the system life cycle. Safeguards are implemented to ensure data integrity and security and to prevent inadvertent loss or modification of data. The performing activity has the responsibility to ensure that the data is collected, stored, controlled, and available for proper configuration management of the evolving product designs, specifications, and baselines. Data-management and design-capture activities should be coordinated.

6.8.2.2 Configuration management

The performing activity plans and implements the functions of

a) Identification of end items to be controlled (through specifications, interface control drawings/documents, and configuration baselines)
b) Control of engineering changes
c) Status accounting
d) Configuration audits

Data pertinent to configuration management are readily accessible throughout the system life cycle. The performing activity establishes and maintains configuration control boards to process, review, and approve engineering changes to end items.

6.8.2.3 Interface management

The performing activity plans and implements the functions of interface definition, interface control, interface compatibility assessments, and interface coordination. Data pertinent to interface management are readily accessible throughout the system life cycle. The performing activity establishes and maintains interface working groups to process, review, and make recommendations on approval of interface changes.

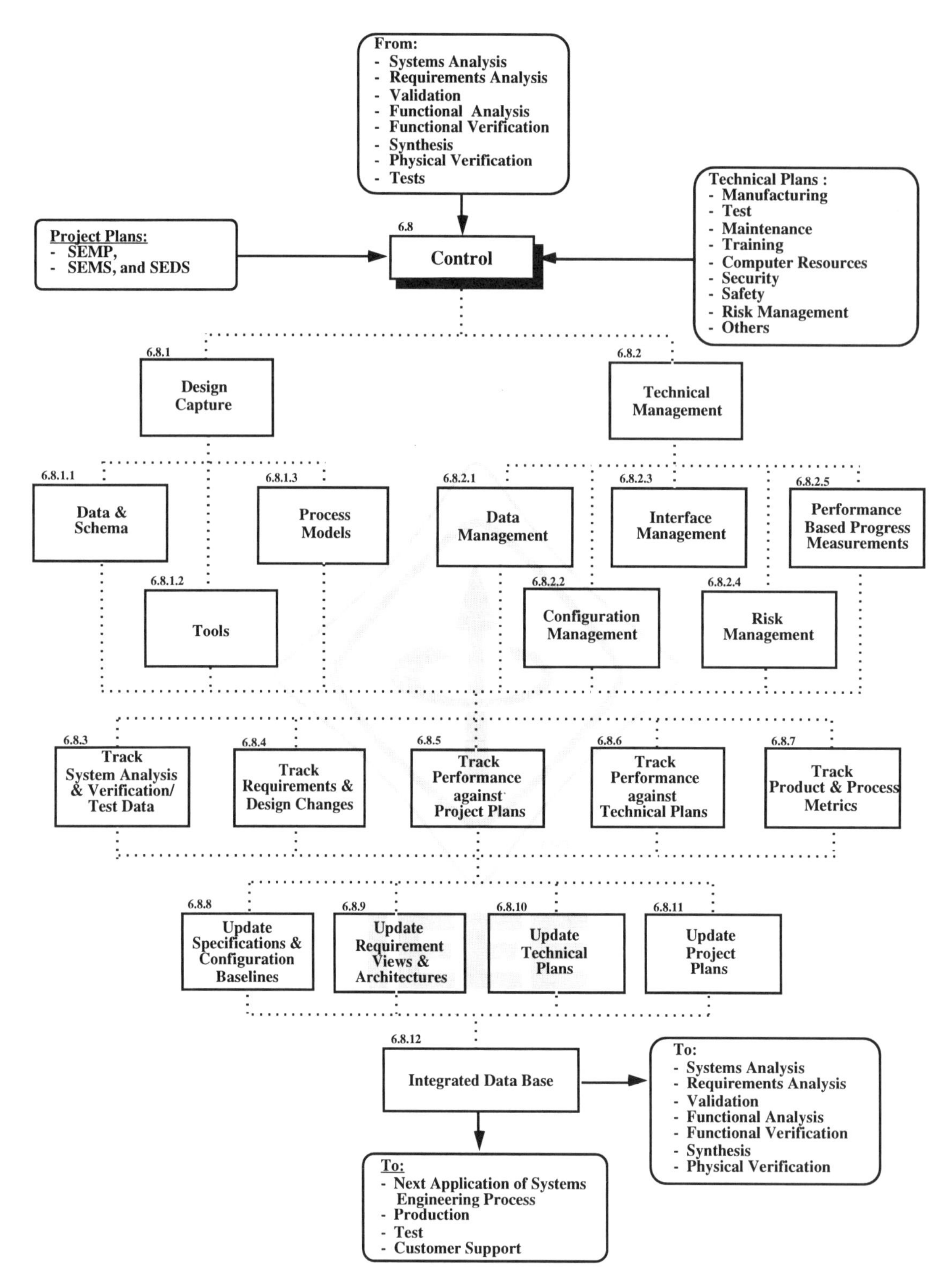

Figure 22—Control process

6.8.2.4 Risk management

A project conducts risk management to systematically control the uncertainty in the project's ability to meet cost, schedule, and performance objectives. The performing activity conducts that part of risk management that directly impacts the systems engineering effort and involves risk management preparation, risk assessment, risk handling option assessment, and risk control. These activities are described below.

a) *Risk management preparation includes*
   1) Identifying acceptable levels of risk for each stage of development
   2) Identifying potential sources of risk
   3) Identifying and evaluating risk management tools and techniques
   4) Training team members to accomplish risk management activities
   5) Deciding on the means by which the analysis and decisions which occur will be documented
   6) Deciding on how risk management information will be captured, processed, and disseminated.
b) *Risk assessment includes*
   1) Identifying and describing those circumstances that might result in adverse effects
   2) Quantifying these circumstances to determine their likelihood and potential cost, schedule, and performance effects
   3) Ranking and integrating these risks to produce a risk assessment for each element of the system breakdown structure appropriate to the stage of development.
c) *Risk handling option assessment* is evaluated to determine those that are feasible and that reduce risks to acceptable levels. Lower-level risk handling options must be integrated with higher-level options that are feasible and that provide the best balance between cost, schedule, performance, and risk for the technical effort and the project.
d) *Risk control* involves continuously assessing risk in order to provide current risk information and to ensure that risk stays within acceptable levels.

6.8.2.5 Performance-based progress measurement

The performing activity measures, evaluates, and tracks the progress of technical efforts with the help of the SEMS, Technical Performance Measurement (TPM), cost and schedule performance measurements, and technical reviews. The activities associated with these measurements are described below.

a) The SEMS identifies tasks and activities, with associated success criteria, of an element of the SBS that must be accomplished to pass a defined technical event. A SEMS provides top-level process control and progress measurements that:
   1) Ensure completion of required technical tasks
   2) Demonstrate progressive achievements and maturity
   3) Ensure that integrated, interdisciplinary information is available for decisions and events
   4) Demonstrate control of cost, schedule, and performance risks in satisfying technical tasks, requirements, and objectives
b) TPMs, when appropriately selected, are key to progressively assessing technical progress. Each critical technical parameter must be tracked relative to time, with dates established as to when progress will be checked, and when full compliance will be met. Key technical parameters are measured relative to lower-level elements of the SBS by estimate, analysis or test, and values rolled up to the system level. TPM is also used to
   1) Assess compliance to requirements
   2) Assess compliance to levels of technical risk
   3) Trigger development of recovery plans for identified deficiencies
   4) Examine marginal cost benefits of performance in excess of requirements

The performing activity reports out-of-tolerance measurements to the project manager so that needed corrective actions may be taken.

c) Cost and schedule performance measurements assess progress based on actual cost of the work performed, the planned cost of the work performed, and the planned cost of the work scheduled. Calculated cost and/or schedule variances quantify the effect of problems being experienced. Cost and schedule performance measurements are integrated with TPMs to provide current cost, schedule, and performance impacts, and to provide an integrated corrective action to variances identified.
d) Technical reviews are conducted at the completion of an application of the systems engineering process and/or end of a stage of development to ensure that all SEMS criteria have been met; assess development maturity to date and the product's ability to satisfy requirements; ensure traceability of requirements and validity of decisions; and assess risks related to, investment needed for, and preparation for the next stage of the life cycle. Clause 5 describes the reviews and audits required and their relationship to life cycle activities.

6.8.3 Systems analysis and test data

The performing activity collects, analyzes, and tracks data from systems analyses to document activities, rationale, recommendations, and impacts. It also collects, analyzes, and tracks data from tests to document results, variances, and follow-up activities.

6.8.4 Requirement and design changes

The performing activity collects and sorts data to track requirement and design changes and to maintain traceability of change source, processing, and approval.

6.8.5 Progress against project plans

The performing activity collects and sorts data reflecting plan activities and tracks progress against the SEMP, SEMS, and SEDS. Deviations from plans and needed changes, shall be requested in advance and shall be undertaken only when approved.

6.8.6 Progress against technical plans

The performing activity collects and sorts data reflecting plan activities and tracks progress against technical plans to determine deviations from plans and needed changes, and to document changes, decisions, and accomplishments.

6.8.7 Product and process metrics

The performing activity collects, analyzes, and tracks product and process metrics to

a) Determine technical areas requiring project management attention
b) Determine the degree of customer satisfaction and public acceptance
c) Provide cost and schedule estimates for new products and provide faster response to customers

Metrics are collected, tracked, and reported at pre-established control points during each stage of development to enable:

— Establishment of a quality system and achievement of efficient use of resources
— Overall system quality and productivity evaluation
— Comparison to planned goals and targets
— Early detection of problems
— Benchmarking of the systems engineering process

6.8.8 Specifications and configuration baselines

The performing activity updates specifications and configuration baselines to reflect all changes approved by the configuration control board. The original configuration baseline, with approved changes, provides the basis for continuing technical efforts.

6.8.9 Requirements views and architectures

The performing activity updates requirements views and the functional, physical, and system architectures to reflect changes brought about by a customer, systems analysis, validation and verification deviation, or management decision. The new validated requirements baseline or verified functional, physical, or system architecture is used for continuing systems engineering process activities.

6.8.10 Project plans

The performing activity updates project plans to reflect changes brought about by a customer, systems analysis, cost or schedule deviation, or management decision. Updates should include systems engineering process and scheduling planning activities for the next stage of the life cycle.

6.8.11 Technical plans

The performing activity updates technical plans to reflect changes brought about by a customer, systems analysis, plan activity deviation, or management decision. Updates should include technical planning activities for the next stage of the life cycle.

6.8.12 Integrated database.

The performing activity prepares and maintains a database to store all pertinent data and information from the tasks in 6.8.1 through 6.8.11. This database is a repository for all information used and generated by the systems engineering process and describes the current state of the system development and its evaluation. An electronic medium is preferred over a manual storage and retrieval database. It should be a sharable database so that all development team participants have access to the data/information needed. The database needs to be accurate, nonambiguous, secure, survivable, easily accessible by authorized users, and complete. The performing activity should regularly back up the database using appropriate media to enable recovery from disaster, failure of equipment or media, or accidental deletion of data.

Annex A
The role of systems engineering within an enterprise

(informative)

A.1 The systems engineering process

The systems engineering process provides a focused approach for product development that attempts to balance all factors associated with product life cycle viability and competitiveness in a global marketplace. This process provides a structured approach for considering alternative design and configurations. Figure A.1 provides a view of the systems engineering process and its role within enterprise and external environments to establish a system design associated with a product offering.

The systems engineering process is applied recursively one level of development at a time. Initially, it is applied to identify the best concept, or approach, to satisfy the market opportunity. This could be a concept for a totally new product/system or a concept for making an incremental improvement to an already established product. The second application of the process adds value to the concept by fully describing the product/system definition and establishing a configuration baseline. This application provides the basis for accomplishing the more detailed engineering development of subsystems, components, and elements of a total system, or the appropriate parts of an established product undergoing incremental improvement during the next application.

A.2 Systems engineering internal to an enterprise

The intent of the portrayal in figure A.1 is to represent systems engineering as the total technical effort responsible for establishing the product design, as well as the concurrent establishment of the development, test, manufacturing, support, operations, training, distribution, and disposal processes. Thus, the term *systems engineering* implies that a total system perspective should be applied to the development of a system. An enterprise must be concerned with two key processes in order to commercialize a product and achieve customer and public acceptance. The systems engineering process establishes the design of the product and its supporting life cycle infrastructure. The manufacturing process transforms raw material, parts, etc., and assembles them into finished products in accordance with product and process data package specifications and instructions. The following subclauses discuss some of the general concepts addressed by figure A.1.

A.2.1 Market opportunity

The enterprise may recognize an opportunity that arises from market research, research and development activities, or technology applications. In such cases, the enterprise is not responding to clearly defined customer requirements or needs, but is attempting to stimulate product acceptance through innovation. In some instances, technological advancement and the system development of this technology provide new market opportunities. Collateral material representing market research or related material pertinent to the product may be available and should establish the customer quality attributes that define a quality product offering within the marketplace. Additionally, an opportunity may arise when an enterprise is contracted to produce a product at the request of a customer. This relationship demands that the enterprise understand the customer's needs and develop a product (in a system context) to satisfy customer and public expectations.

A.2.2 New technological advances

New technologies may have a broad effect on the performance and capabilities of new products. Thus, as an input to the requirements process, new technologies must be assessed for their value to improving the product's design or capability.

A.2.3 Project environment

The project environment defines the objectives, success criteria, project milestones, and associated management priorities that will govern the integrated technical activities in support of product development. The methods by which the project is to be accomplished within the project environment should be documented in a systems integrated management plan. The efficiency and effectiveness of project integrated technical activities are enhanced by integrated, multidisciplinary teamwork and appropriate computer-aided integrated tools.

A.2.4 Enterprise environment

The enterprise establishes the policies and procedures that govern project activities associated with product development. Additionally, enterprise standards and general specifications or guidelines govern development activities and product designs. These directives represent enterprise guidelines for establishing a viable product in a competitive marketplace. Enterprise management will typically allocate the resources available to accomplish the project systems engineering tasks and activities in support of establishing the product design, manufacturing, test, operations, support distribution, training, and disposal processes. Enterprise activities include the training of project personnel, establishing key application technologies, and implementing the enterprise information infrastructure for control of projects. The domain technologies of the enterprise also constrain tool availability and use, design alternatives, and process solutions.

A.2.5 External environment

The external environment provides the political and social opinions or constraints that affect enterprise endeavors to commercialize new products. The enterprise must ensure that the product is designed to be compliant with applicable socio-political constraints. These constraints constitute the socio-political climate under which commercial or industrial activities are regulated and include environmental protection regulations, safety regulations, technological constraints, and other regulations established by federal and local government agencies to protect the interests of consumers. Additionally, international, government, and industry standards and general specifications constrain enterprise and project activities and design options. Competitor products must be understood by the enterprise in order to set benchmarks for improving their product designs or make the decision not to compete in a given product area. Another constraint on product solutions is provided by the natural and induced environments in which a product will operate. The impact of these environments, as well as the impact a given product will have on these environments, establish to a large extent the public acceptability of the product in the marketplace.

A.2.6 Products

A basic interest of an enterprise is to market products that satisfy customer expectations and have general public acceptance. Acceptance includes having the applicable services of distribution, training, support, and disposal available when needed to sustain product use.

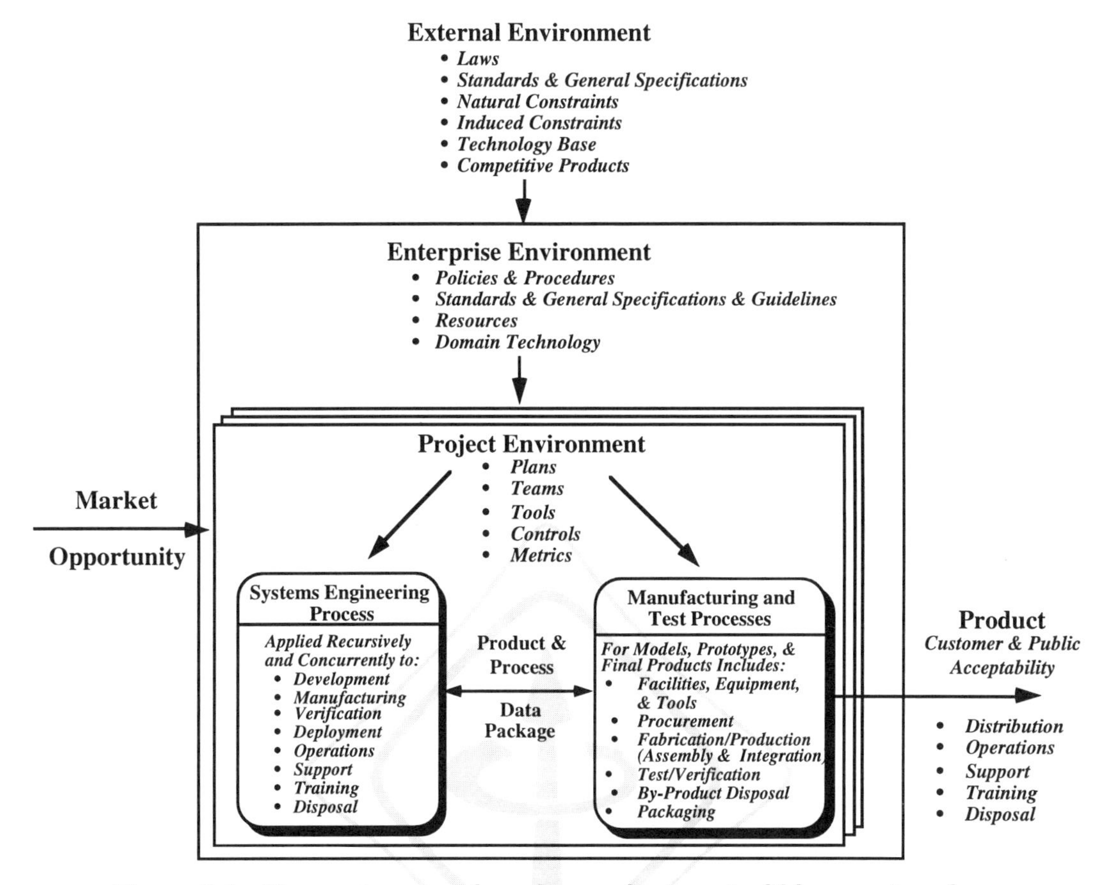

Figure A.1—The systems engineering environment within an enterprise

A.3 The systems engineering problem and solution space

In this context, systems engineering is responsible for the total development effort necessary to establish a product design that can be tested, manufactured, supported, operated, distributed, and disposed of. Also, the training for operation, support, distribution (installation, etc.), and disposal must be accounted for. The challenge of engineering a system to satisfy the combination of customer expectations; enterprise policies; and social, legal, and geo-political restrictions requires a structured process for exploring options in system alternatives to ensure that a cost-effective, practical design is developed. Figure A.2 depicts the problem space that must be explored and well understood in order to begin developing a product solution.

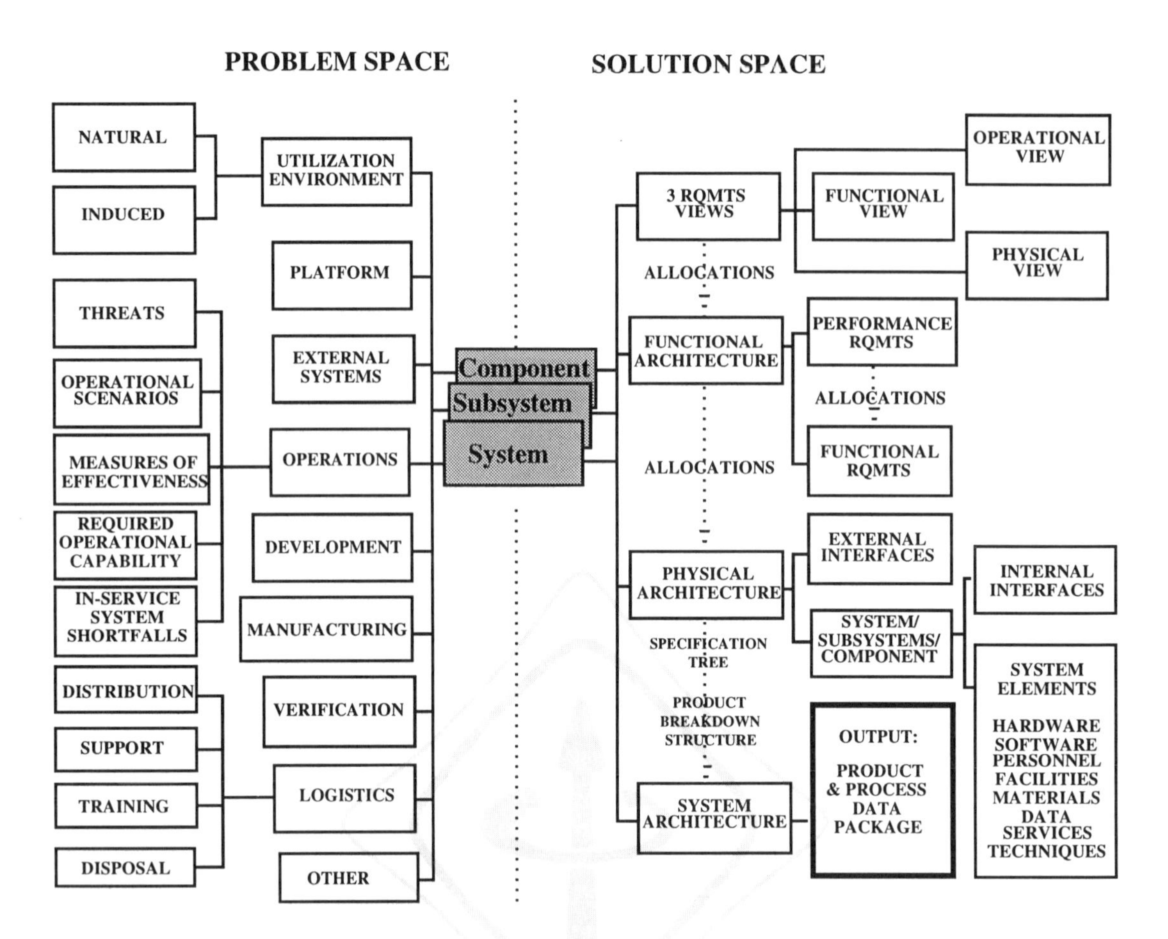

Figure A.2—The problem and solution space for systems engineering

Annex B
The Systems Engineering Management Plan (SEMP)

(informative)

B.1 Systems Engineering Management Plan (SEMP) template

The purpose of this SEMP template is to provide an enterprise with a format for preparing a systems engineering management plan. Typically, a project has a project-specific SEMP for each stage of development and uses it to guide and track systems engineering activities. The project-specific SEMP must be compliant with project management plans; enterprise plans, capabilities, and constraints; and customer expectations.

Since each project may have unique life cycle dimensions, tolerance for risk, and need for data, the SEMP must be tailored for each application.

B.2 SEMP structure

The SEMP is a living document and needs to be structured to allow for ease of updating to reflect changes and progress throughout a stage of the life cycle. Frequently changed data may be collected in a table. Process flows or organizations that will change may be collected in an annex. The data that requires high-level approval to change should be separate from that which the performing activity may change. A configuration management plan for the SEMP should be included in the SEMP. Information should not be duplicated in multiple sections. A simple cross reference would be helpful in appropriate sections. As a guide to a preparer, typical sections are provided in this recommended template structure. What each section and subsection should contain is in italic.

Title Page

Include the words "Systems Engineering Management Plan," the document control number for the project, organization involved, and the document title and/or applicable system. Figure B.1 provides an example of a title page with the necessary information identified.

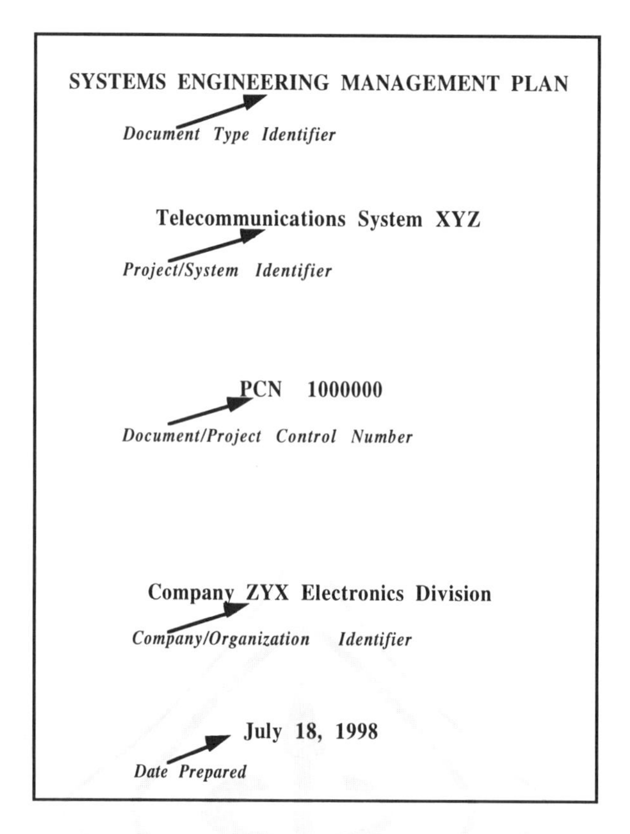

Figure B.1—Example title page

Table of Contents

List the title and page number of each section and subsection. The table of contents should also list the title and page number of each figure, table, and appendix, in that order. Note that page numbers below represent template references only. No document length is inferred or implied. Figure B.2 provides an example of a table of contents.

Table of Contents

Figure B.2—Example table of contents

Section 1—Scope

Include a brief description of the purpose of the system to which the SEMP applies and a summarization of the purpose and content of the SEMP and how its configuration will be managed.

Section 2—Applicable documents

List all government, international or American national standards, industry, enterprise, project, and other directive documents applicable to the conduct of the tasks within the SEMP.

Section 3—Systems engineering process and application

Describe the tasking/performing activity's systems engineering process activities as they are to be applied to the total engineering effort of the project. It also should describe the organizational responsibilities and authority for systems engineering activities, including control of supplier engineering. Descriptions include the tasks needed to satisfy each accomplishment criteria identified in the Systems Engineering Master Schedule (SEMS) and the milestones and schedules of the Systems Engineering Detailed Schedule (SEDS) for the project. Descriptions include narratives, supplemented as necessary by graphical presentations, which detail the plans, processes, and procedures for the application of the systems engineering process.

Subsection 3.1—Systems engineering process planning

Briefly give an overview of the key project technical objectives, deliverables, and results from the process, needed process inputs, and product work breakdown structure development.

Subsection 3.1.1—Major deliverables and results

Describe in detail the major technical deliverables and results both to the customer and internal organizations within Company X *as a result of the systems engineering process activities.*

Subsection 3.1.1.1—Integrated database

Describe the implementation of the decision database. Include a description of how information will be captured, traced, and maintained. Provide a description of the provisioning for design capture data/schema to include domain models (processes, technologies, etc.); product models (physical prototypes—location, availability, characterization, etc.); archival data (lessons learned, past designs, empirical data); requirements, goals and constraints; project management models (cost, schedule, and risk); integrated views, multiple views, and multidisciplinary designs and their rationale; trade studies and system/cost effectiveness analysis rationale and results; verification data; and product and process metrics.

Subsection 3.1.1.2 —Specifications and baselines

Describe how the generation of specifications and baselines will be documented and controlled.

Subsection 3.1.2—Process inputs

Identify the depth of detailed information needed to be able to accomplish the activities (appropriate to the level of development) of the systems engineering process, how needed information will be acquired, and how conflicts will be resolved.

Subsection 3.1.3—Technical objectives

Describe the technical objectives related to success of the project, system, and system effectiveness e.g., Customer Measures Of Effectiveness (MOEs). Technical objectives may include those related to the system products and their life cycle processes.

Subsection 3.1.4—System Breakdown Structure (SBS)

Describes how the elements of the system breakdown structure will be developed. The relationship of the specification tree and the drawing tree with the elements of the SBS and how the system products and their life cycle processes will be related should be explained. This subsection should describe for each element of the SBS the methods for development and control of work packages; development of planning packages and their conversion to work packages; sizing of work packages; resource use, including integrated product teams; traceability of changes; cost reporting and its integration to scheduling and critical path identification; and configuration management.

Subsection 3.1.5—Training

Identify both internal and external (suppliers/customers) training needed. Include analysis of performance or behavior deficiencies or shortfalls, required training to remedy, and schedules to achieve required proficiencies.

Subsection 3.1.6—Standards and procedures

Describe major standards and procedures that the project will follow. Incorporate implementation of standardization tasking into pertinent sections of the systems engineering process below.

Subsection 3.1.7—Resource allocation

Describe the method of resource allocation to project technical tasks. Include resource requirements identification, procedures for resource control, and reallocation procedures.

Subsection 3.1.8—Constraints

Describe major constraints on the project. Include those things the project cannot or will not do. Also include funding, personnel, facilities, manufacturing capability/capacity, critical resources, or other constraints.

Subsection 3.1.9—Work authorization

Describe the method by which work is authorized to be performed within the project. Also describe the method by which changes to work efforts will be authorized.

Subsection 3.2—Requirements analysis

Document the approach and methods for analysis of system product uses, utilization environments, performance expectations, and design constraints and identification of needs, requirements, and constraints related to life cycle processes. Also document the approach and methods to be used to define the functional and performance requirements for the following quality factors—producibility, testability and integrated diagnostics, distributability (including packaging and handling, transportability, and installability), supportability, trainability, and disposability; and for the following engineering specialty areas—reliability, maintainability, electromagnetic compatibility and electrostatic discharge, human engineering and human systems integration, safety, health hazards and environmental impact, system security, infrastructure support and any other engineering specialty bearing on the determination of functional and performance requirements for the system for the appropriate level of development. Additionally, describe the approach and methods for evolving system products.

NOTE—Some areas may impact requirements analysis only after synthesis efforts identify physical solution alternatives. Some of the descriptive information may be more appropriately covered under other systems engineering process activities.)

Subsection 3.3—Requirements baseline validation

Include the approach and methods to validate that the requirements baseline established from requirements analysis is both upward and downward traceable to customer expectations, project and enterprise constraints, and external constraints.

Subsection 3.4—Functional analysis

Include a description of the approach and methods planned to determine lower-level functions, allocate performance and other limiting requirements to lower-level functions, define functional interfaces, and define the functional architecture. Define also approaches and methods for the quality factors and engineering specialty areas discussed in subsection 3.2.

Subsection 3.5—Functional verification

Include a description of the approach and methods planned to verify that the functional architecture established from functional analysis is both upward and downward traceable to the validated requirements baseline.

Subsection 3.6—Synthesis

Include the approach and methods to transform the functional architecture into a physical architecture, to define alternative system concepts, to define physical interfaces, and to select preferred product and process solutions. Describe how requirements are converted into detailed design specifications. Define also approaches and methods for the quality factors and engineering specialty areas discussed in subsection 3.2. In addition, include the following areas—nondevelopmental items and parts control.

Subsection 3.7—Physical verification

Include a description of the approach and methods planned to verify that the physical architecture established from synthesis is both upward and downward traceable to the functional architecture and satisfies the requirements of the validated requirements baseline.

Subsection 3.8—Systems analysis

Include an overview of the approach and methods planned to be utilized to arrive at a balanced set of requirements and balanced functional and physical architecture to satisfy those requirements and control the level of development-dependent outputs of the systems engineering process. Provides an overview of the specific systems analysis efforts needed. Include methods and tools for trade studies, systems and cost effectiveness analyses, and risk management.

Subsection 3.8.1—Trade studies

Describe the studies planned to make trade-offs among stated requirements, design, project schedule, functional and performance requirements, and life cycle/design-to-cost objectives. Describe the use of criteria for decision making and trade-off of alternative physical solutions. Include a description of technical objectives, criteria and weighting factors, and utility curves as applicable. Also describe the methods and tools planned to be used and the integration of trade study data into the integrated database.

Subsection 3.8.2—System and cost effectiveness analyses

Describe the implementation of system and cost effectiveness analyses to support the development of life cycle balanced products and processes and to support risk management. Describe the Measures Of Effectiveness (MOEs), how they interrelate and criteria for the selection of Measures Of Performance (MOPs) to support the evolving definition and verification of the system. Include description of the overall approach for system/cost effectiveness analysis as well as manufacturing analysis, verification analysis, distribution analysis, operational analysis, supportability analysis, training analysis, environmental analysis, and life cycle cost analysis. Describe how analytic results will be integrated.

Subsection 3.8.3—Risk management

Describe the technical risk program, including the approach, methods, procedures, and criteria for risk assessment (identification and quantification) and selection of the risk handling options and integration into the decision process. Also describe the risks associated with the development and verification requirements. Identify critical risk areas. Describe plans to minimize technical risks (additional prototyping, technology and integration verification, evolutionary system development). Identify risk control and monitoring measures, including special verifications, technical performance measure parameters, and critical milestones/ events. Describe the method of relating TPM, the SEMS, and the SEDS to cost and schedule performance measurement and the relationship to the system breakdown structure.

Subsection 3.9—Control

Provide an overview of plans for design capture, interface management, data management, event-based scheduling, calendar-based scheduling, technical performance measurement, technical reviews, supplier control, and requirements traceability.

Subsection 3.9.1—Design capture

Describe the approach and methods planned to manage the system definition (configuration) of identified system products and the related life cycle process products for manufacturing, verification, distribution, support, training, and disposal. Include a description of change management, configuration control procedures, and baseline management. Describe the design record for alternatives, trade studies, decisions/conclusions, and lessons learned.

Subsection 3.9.2—Interface management

Describe the approach and methods planned to manage the internal interfaces appropriate to the level of development to ensure that external interfaces (external to the project or at a higher level of the functional or physical architecture) are managed and controlled. Include description of change management and the interrelationship with configuration control procedures.

Subsection 3.9.3—Data management

Describe the approach and methods planned to establish and maintain a data management system and the interrelationship with the design capture system and decision database. Include descriptions of how and which technical documentation will be controlled and the method of documentation of project engineering and technical information. Describe plans for security and preparation of deliverable data.

Subsection 3.9.4—Systems Engineering Master Schedule (SEMS)

Describe the critical path methodology and criteria for event transition used to derive the SEMS and supporting Systems Engineering Detailed Schedule (SEDS) and their structure. Include a description of the approach and methods planned to update and maintain both the SEMS and the SEDS.

Subsection 3.9.5—Technical performance measurement

Describe the approach and methods to identify, establish, and control key technical parameters (limited to those that are critical and/or identified by the customer). Descriptions include the thresholds, methods of measuring and tracking, update frequencies, level of tracking depth, and response time to generate recovery plans and planned profile revisions. Described parameters include identification of related risks. Describe the relationship between the selected parameter and lower-level parameters that must be measured to determine the critical parameter achievement value is depicted in the form of tiered dependency trees and reflect the tie-in to the related system performance requirement (critical parameter). Include definition of the correlation of each parameter in the dependency tree to a specific system breakdown structure element.

Subsection 3.9.6—Technical reviews

Describe the technical reviews and/or audits (system, subsystem, component, and life cycle process,) applicable to the level(s) of development covered by the SEMP. Describe the approach and procedures planned to complete identified reviews and/or audits. Describe the tasks associated with the conduct of each review, including responsibilities of personnel involved and necessary procedures (e.g., action item close out procedures). Include a description of how

- *a) Compliance with the tasking activity SEMP/SEMS and/or this SEMP and performing activity SEMS will be determined*
- *b) The discrepancies identified as not meeting SEMP/SEMS requirements will be handled*
- *c) System products and related life cycle process products assessed to have a moderate-to-high risk of compliance will be addressed prior to conducting the review*

Subsection 3.9.7—Supplier control

Describe the technical control of suppliers and vendors. Include the approach and methods to flow down requirements, manage interfaces, control quality, build long-term relationships, and assure participation on integrated product teams.

Subsection 3.9.8—Requirements traceability

Describe how requirements traceability will be implemented. Include the traceability between systems engineering process activities, system breakdown structures, and correlation, as pertinent, with the SEMS and the SEDS. Describe the interrelationship of requirements traceability with data management and the integrated database.

Section 4—Transitioning critical technologies

Describe the approach and methods for identifying key technologies and their associated risks. Describe the activities and criteria for assessing and transitioning critical technologies from technology development and demonstration projects internal to the enterprise or from suppliers or other sources. Describe how alternatives will be identified and selection criteria established to determine when and which alternative technology will be incorporated into the product when moderate-to-high risk technologies are assessed as required to meet functional and performance requirements. Describe the planned method for engineering and technical process improvement, including procedures for establishing an evolutionary system development to enable an incremental improvement approach for system products as technologies mature or for evolution of the system.)

Section 5—Integration of the systems engineering effort

Describe how the various inputs into the systems engineering effort will be integrated and how integrated product teaming will be implemented to integrate appropriate disciplines into a coordinated systems engineering effort that meets cost, schedule, and performance objectives. Give a brief description of the approach and methods planned to assure integration of the engineering specialties to meet project objectives.

Subsection 5.1—Organizational structure

Describe how the organizational structure will support teaming. Describe the composition of teams organized to support a specific element of the system breakdown structure. Also describe major responsibilities and authority of team members by name, and include present and planned project technical staffing. Include planned personnel needs by discipline and performance level, human resource loading, and identification of key personnel.

Subsection 5.2—Required systems engineering integration tasks

Describe the approach and methods for systems engineering integration tasks such as: technology verification, process proofing, fabrication of engineering test articles, development test and evaluation, implementation of software designs for system products, customer and supplier engineering, and problem-solving support.

Section 6—Additional systems engineering activities

Give a brief description of other areas not specifically covered in sections 1 through 5, but essential for planning a total systems engineering effort. Give a brief description of additional systems engineering activities essential to successfully engineering a total system solution.

Subsection 6.1—Long-lead items

Describe the long-lead items that affect the critical path of the project.

Subsection 6.2—Engineering tools

Describe the systems engineering methods and tools that are planned to be implemented on the program to support systems engineering. Identify those tools to be acquired and training requirements.

Subsection 6.3—Design to cost

Describe the design to cost planning and how cost will be implemented and controlled as a design parameter.

Subsection 6.4—Value engineering

Describe the approach and methods planned to address value engineering throughout the development cycle.

Subsection 6.5—Systems integration plan

Describe the approach and methods by which the system is assembled and integrated.

Subsection 6.6—Interface with other life cycle support functions

Describe the approach and methods to assure compatibility with other life cycle support functions consistent with project and enterprise plans.

Subsection 6.7—Other plans and controls

Describe the approach and methods for any other plans and controls designated the tasking activity or which the Performing Activity system architect, systems engineer, or system integrator will use.

Subsection 6.8—Configuration management of the SEMP

Describe how this SEMP will be configuration controlled.

Section 7—Notes

Should contain any general information that aids in understanding the SEMP (e.g., background information; alphabetical listing of all acronyms, abbreviations, and their meanings as used in the SEMP; and glossary of terms used). Explain which of the items in this section are mandatory or are provided for general information.

Subsection 7.1—General background information

Provide background information that will help the implementors and managers of the activities and tasks of this SEMP better understand and accomplish their responsibilities.

Subsection 7.2—Acronyms and abbreviations

Provide an alphabetical list of acronyms and abbreviations and their meanings.

Subsection 7.3—Glossary

Provide an alphabetical listing of key terms and their applied meaning within the context of this SEMP.

Appendices

Appendices should be included as necessary to provide information published separately for convenience in document maintenance. Included should be charts and proprietary data applicable to the systems engineering efforts required in the SEMP. Also included in an annex would be a summary of technical plans associated with the project. Each annex should be referenced in one of the sections of the SEMP where data would normally have been provided.

IEEE

IEEE

IEEE

IEEE

IEEE